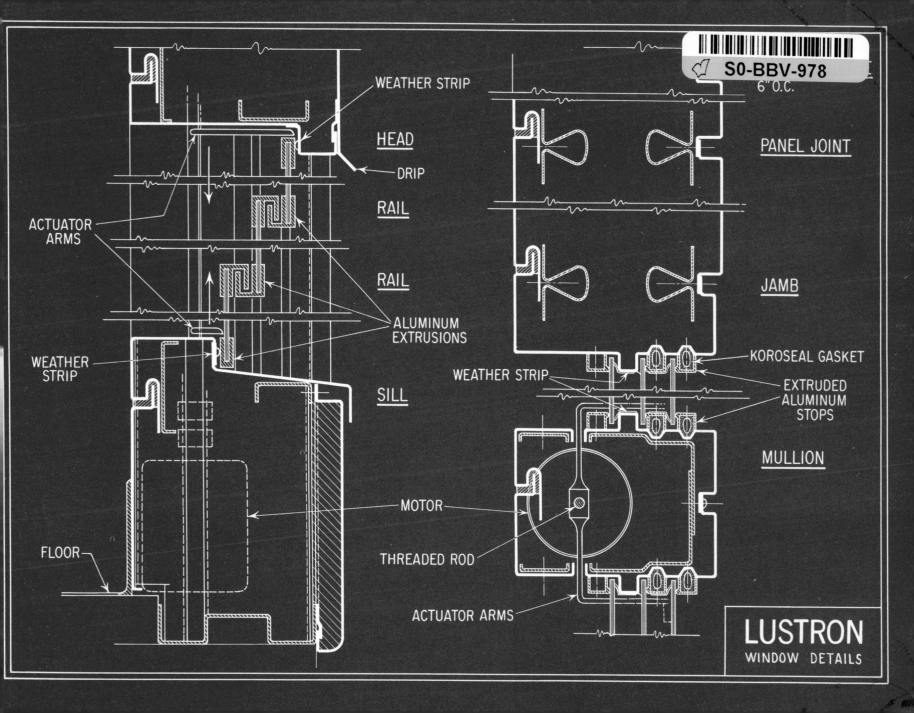

WEATHER STRIP

HEAD

DRIP

RAIL

ACTUATOR ARMS

RAIL

ALUMINUM EXTRUSIONS

WEATHER STRIP

SILL

FLOOR

PANEL JOINT

JAMB

6" O.C.

KOROSEAL GASKET

WEATHER STRIP

EXTRUDED ALUMINUM STOPS

MULLION

MOTOR

THREADED ROD

ACTUATOR ARMS

LUSTRON
WINDOW DETAILS

AT HOME WITH TOMORROW

AT HOME WITH

RINEHART & COMPANY, INC.   NEW YORK   TORONTO

TOMORROW

by CARL KOCH, designer of the Techbuilt House

WITH ANDY LEWIS

Published simultaneously in Canada by
Clarke, Irwin & Company, Ltd., Toronto

Copyright © 1958 by Carl Koch and Andy Lewis
Printed in the United States of America
Library of Congress Catalog Card Number: 58-5160

Introduction

I would like to explain why Andy Lewis and I have undertaken *another* book on houses and to say a few words explaining how we went about it together.

As an architect I have realized that what a civilization builds expresses its beliefs and aspirations—its meaning. I feel strongly that two outstanding meanings of civilization are the provision of equal opportunity and the elimination of want. Here in America now, we believe that both aims are finally possible of realization. The house of the average man is certainly a better place to look for the visual realization of these ideals than in our commercial, religious, or civic centers. Therefore, the provision of everyman's house and his living community has seemed to me, as an architect living in America today, the most interesting job to tackle.

But to build a house for everyman, we must use the facility which is making it possible for us to reach these objectives: equal opportunity and elimination of poverty. This facility is industrialized mass production.

And there is an understandable reluctance on the part of everyman to build his castle of nuts, bolts, and chromium. The industrial revolution will help us realize our dreams if we can handle it, but we haven't handled it too well so far. Although it is pathetic to think we can escape the pressure of competitive business, the battle of home-office transportation, and the compulsion to drive ourselves too far, too fast, too much, by escaping into a fantasy in the shape of an eighteenth-century farmhouse, it is understandable that we try.

This book is written with the hope that the experiences recorded herein may help everyman (at least a valid sample of him) to take a little more objective and affirmative look at his living problems and opportunities. For he, the customer, must make an affirmative demand for a living environment worthy of his real aspirations. The builder only builds what he thinks this customer wants to buy. Only by his making this affirmative demand will we designers, producers, and builders be able to devote the time, effort, and inspiration necessary to produce an affirmative answer: a castle for everyman.

I first met Andy Lewis when I was a member of a group of professors, engineers, and other assorted house hunters who finally launched Conantum, a community described in this book.

Subsequently he, as an idea man for the Ford Foundation Radio and Television Workshop, persuaded the Workshop that the designing and building of a house would make an educational and entertaining subject for one of its programs. Our Techbuilt house (as later described) became the subject of this tale.

I soon came to admire the clear, simple way Andy revealed the intricate and devious process of designing and building a house in this program.

During this time we became very good friends. One convivial evening we decided to do a program together on the good life through design. For some time after this I took to writing him a postcard now and then when the desire to relate the good life to design was particularly strong, like in an airplane twelve thousand feet up on a clear, frosty morning over Vermont, or on a summer evening at the flea circus at Tivoli Gardens in Copenhagen. This didn't get us much further along, however. Nevertheless, Andy always seemed to know what I was talking about and, if the truth must be told, sometimes explained to me what it was I would be talking about, if I knew!

So it was quite easy for me to make the practical suggestion that we write a book together where I would do all the heavy talking and all he'd have to do was the rest.

I am very grateful indeed to him for agreeing. I'd also like to emphasize my gratitude to all the clients, starting with my father and mother and including my wife, who had suffered with my mistakes; and to my associates, who have contributed, often anonymously, to whatever success we have achieved.

Contents

AT HOME WITH TOMORROW

1 What Is a House?

There was a time, obviously, when the way to a house was simple. Your neolithic ancestor either dug one for himself or found someone else who already had, and put him out of the way.

Today you must proceed differently. And the strait way is laced with lawyers, bankers, the editors of home magazines, building commissioners, suppliers, builders—and architects. It may appear that we are working as a group to deprive you of your fundamental rights— we are, in fact, though somewhat despite ourselves. Nowadays this is called "teamwork" and is highly regarded. In the old days it was called conspiracy, and wasn't.

In the midst of the cheerful, contractual mayhem of this century, it is a rare family who persist toward building the house they most deeply want. And want, in the deepest sense. That house which, over a period of years, will shelter them adequately, will change in function to suit their changing needs, will set them in a useful relationship to their community, and assist rather than direct them in the business of living. Such families are rare— happily they increase; to them this book is directed. It is dedicated to all those I malign along the way, and to those past clients who have willingly served themselves up on the altar of research.

I remember a family doctor of my youth who, having peered inside me, tuned in his stethoscope to the noises I made, and shaken his head doubtfully to indicate the odds he labored against, would rummage about in a bagful of materia medica and produce, invariably, the same noxious bottled medicine he had prescribed before. He would exhibit it to me with the kind of specious cheerfulness which may deceive a man of three but not one of five. "This," he would say, "isn't really so awful. I mean to say, it isn't bad at all. That is, in fact, you'll *like* it; you'll think it tastes good. Yum."

I do not remember ever believing the doctor, or being taken in by the bright color of the potion itself. On the other hand—after my parents had run me to ground, held my arms and legs, and forced it inside me—as a healthy child I always recovered.

Most people, I think, including many architects, now look upon the prefabricated house as I looked on that bottle then: inevitable, perhaps, vaguely beneficial, but in and of itself unpleasant. A bitter medicine which they would just as soon have someone else swallow; a medicine which will have to be administered, at any rate, without their personal cooperation.

Prefabrication is, indeed, a specific for some of our housing ills. But I hope to show—on better evidence than the doctor's—that it is a good deal more than that. In it lies a hope of happy, healthy—"good"—surroundings for many millions of families. For most individual families, for the first time in history, it may afford the opportunity of building the kind of house which they have only talked of heretofore. The shortcomings of prefabricated houses have been many. The failures of their producers have been frequent, in some cases spectacular. But the industry is on a sound footing, with necessity behind it. And the setbacks along the way need not lead us into fixed ideas about the advantages or disadvantages of prefabrication, or of the ways the industrial house is bound to "look." Because it is made in a factory, it need not imitate the factory. Neither is it the formalized, hen-coop affair that many think of, nor need it have the mechanized, dehumanized look of a Sunday-supplement drawing of the future. It will come—and comes—in a variety of shapes, appearances, and materials, increasingly characterized by good sense, good artistry, soundness of construction, and economy.

While the first concern of this book is with the single, industrialized house, there are many attendant concerns which are mentioned in later chapters: the relation of house to land and community; the interests of the family—especially the women of the family—in selecting and making use of their home; the history and present state of prefabrication as an industry and the difficulties against which it works; and, finally, the ways in which I believe architectural design is, or must be, influenced by the broad characteristics of these times. Since I have worked for some years in the general area of prefabrication, much of what follows, particularly in the later chapters, is in the nature of a personal narrative. And not an unfailingly happy one. But my purpose throughout is to make clear the reasoning behind the industrialized house, the ways in which it has worked, or failed to work, and the use you or your children may want to make of it.

The mainstream of architecture is set about by the fever trees of art, engineering, economics, personal habit, and social reform. The architect himself must function as a cut-rate psychiatrist, budgeteer, social arbiter, and conspicuous waster. So, as it comes about, he never lacks for advice on what people need, or believe they need, and what a house must be. From all this, you would think, he would learn to keep his own modest peace. And yet, in his off hours, he is as noisy as anyone else. And though a house, by and large, tends to be recognizable as such, time and again the architect scrooches up his eyes, and tries to see it "for what it is." And spins out long, delicate theories concerning its "real" nature—as springing from the earth, for instance, organic, growing. Or, on the other hand, as having nothing to do with the earth—mechanical, crystallic—or descended lightly from the skies, like a wilted balloon. As expressing its inhabitants, or various human functions, the state of its innards, or the materials of which it is made.

(In the meantime, of course, eighty-five per cent of all houses are conceived and executed not by architects at all, but builders—who in many cases have never heard of Van der Rohe, Wright, or Le Corbusier, but who know by sure, uncluttered calculation when the building inspector would like his next case of bourbon.)

These various contradictory admonitions have certain common characteristics. First: They issue from fine architects, who have done splendid works—and would have done them in any case—and whose works will remain splendid long after their theoristic filigree has weathered off. Second: As theories, they are most vigorously bandied about by the high-minded residents of 1890 walk-up apartments—to whom it apparently never occurs that the proper, first business of architecture might be to get them and their children *out* of the 1890 walk-up, into a good house at a decent price.

At this point, having spoken against this type of theorizing, I must offer my own list of the principles or purposes or essentials of the family house. *Not* to demonstrate how much they prescribe for the planning of houses, but in certain respects how little. There are very few things a house *must* be. And most houses, even the poorest, are. A house is:

1. A way to keep the weather off.

This naturally includes not only the up-and-down kinds of weather—rain or snow—but the sideways kind, like wind. In most climates, it suggests an enclosed rather than an umbrella shape. As a single requirement, of course, it might be met by a sort of blanket or overcoat. But a house is also:

2. A place to beget and raise children.

For the latter purpose, at least, an overcoat will not suffice. Human young, in fact, are remarkable among species for the amount of space and special equipment they require. And the length of time for which they remain—though lovable—vulnerable and useless. How might we house ourselves, indeed, if they matured in a year's time, and our womankind, in consequence, were differently geared?

3. A defense against unfriendly humans, and animals of all sizes—especially at night.

This specification clearly has less force now than in times past, when the home owner—the pueblo builder, by example—fortified himself so well that he scarcely could get in or out. Yet I am inclined to believe, from experience with clients, that we all harbor dim racial memories of attack and defense—fears neither practical nor easily expressed, but acting as hidden imperatives to our choices of walls and corners, and the shape of rooms in which we individually like to find ourselves.

Practically, of course, there is a legitimate present concern for common defense against atomic weapons. Taken seriously, this might have broad effect in a housing program—planned dispersion of dwellings, the use of demountable houses, and the like. About it, nothing effective has yet been done. Or is likely to be.

4. A place to bring, prepare, and eat food.

This requires no special comment, save to note that the size, shape, positioning, *and* cost, of kitchen and dining space—and more recently bathroom—go a long way toward determining the plan of any small house. With ideal considerations quite aside.

At the same time a house is:

5. Buildable, makeable—the more easily so the better. This implies also obtainable, buyable, cheap.

6. More or less durable.

This pertains not only to the strength of materials and joints—the simple desideratum that a house remain upright for a given length of time—but to many more subtle things. The durability of its *value,* for one, its continued salability. And this consideration extends from the house outward to the lot, community, and countryside around it, into the large land uses which in time will make it worth more or less. Here are invisible, overlapping boundaries of lives and houses—matters infinitely complex, generally disregarded, full of dour implications for our traditional ways of life, and day by day more desperately important. Topics of regional, urban, and community design are becoming central to all architectural thought.

7. Variously comfortable, or even pleasant, to be *in.*

This last point is perhaps the only one which borders on the aesthetic, and even here I have in mind, first, the gross requirement that the house be big enough to stand *up* in, and that its facilities be conveniently located. I don't mean to minimize the consideration of beauty—that's where the fun is—but to suggest that it comes somewhat in addition to these other things, and has emerged from them, as often as not, by way of instinct. Some manifestations of beauty—those with which an architect is most usefully concerned—do not inhere in formal elements, but in the things which he assists to happen in and around the house, the character of family living which his design may serve to encourage.

If we are willing to accept the seven points above as the elementary first purposes of any house, what we may find remarkable is how little, artistically or technically, they specify what we must do. Our capacities to house ourselves—in all but the meanest of circumstances —have reached beyond the minimum requirements of shelter. If, as we know to be the case, our shelter is nevertheless unsatisfactory to us, it may be that we may find the causes in factors which are external in space to our private dwelling places, and extended in time beyond the first design or building of them. And if we share a common obligation to house ourselves well, it may be that we can help to satisfy it by an intelligent application of those principles of production which have provided well for us in other respects. We may find, also, that the architect, having means to accomplish much, does better to make a systematic, humanly directed use of his materials than to employ them as tiddlywinks in private, precious aesthetic games (when he has the opportunity of choosing, that is).

We are rich in materials. Take wood as a literal example: Wonderful stuff to begin with. The ancients, and our own pioneers, hacked their wood down, dragged it to the building

---

place, and bruted it into convenient lengths. Later, it was professionally cut, sawed, cured, stacked, and merchandised. Nowadays, we do a hundred more devious and profitable things with it: peel and laminate it, chip and glue, explode and press it, into substances as flexible as rope or as durable as metal. We pulverize it and turn it into paper, and from paper back into intricate shapes and combinations—even, finally, make it back into walls, light enough to lift, but more resistant to sound and heat and several times stronger than the board we might have started with.

But our wealth of resources applies not only to materials and technical processes—plastic pipe, soil cements, heat pumps, and all the like—it extends to the amount of statistical, sociological, and economic material available to both architect and planner, the ways in which problems may be conceptualized, and our ability to foresee the course of new energies. And we have been rich enough in these things to be careless of them. Finally, with the filling up of our land, we are made aware of an ugliness in our cities and towns which we suppose we must have allowed to happen, but can't remember exactly how—an illogic between the way things might be and the way, in fact, they are.

The illogic is sharpest when we consider the change in character of our population over the last fifty years, the ways in which it has distributed itself, and the skill at its disposal. To make the example: Let us suppose that you, for these fifty years, have been sitting on a small asteroid in the vicinity of Smith County, Kansas. Let us suppose further that, although you are high enough to oversee the whole of the United States, your eyesight is so remark-ably keen as to single out the little dots which are people, the larger dots which are their conveyances, the lines of roads, the squares of houses and factories, and masses of cities. As you sit there, what has happened below?

First, of course, a great increase in the *number* of dots (people) from a population of seventy-six million in 1900 to more than twice that today. And a gradual settling out toward the West, though the population center of the country, in Illinois, is still six hundred miles east of where you sit. Second, and more dramatic, you've seen a tremendous increase in the activity, the mobility, of the population. This has come mostly, of course, with the automobile —of which there were a few thousand in 1900 and around forty million now, or more than enough for all of us to be riding at once. We travel around five hundred billion miles a year, over the road. Even our railroads, though they do not prosper, have doubled their trackage in fifty years.

Now, as to the groupings of dots—here two things have been happening. First of all, like iron filings, they have been drawn to the magnetic centers of cities. Since 1900, the metropolitan population has grown by sixty-five millions, and the rural population by less than ten. In the decade between 1940 and 1950, for instance, the population gain of metro-politan areas was 22 per cent. If the trend continues, by the year 2050 the United States population of three hundred million will be 90 per cent urbanized. Each of our cities will be tripled in size. To make the problem more immediate: Within the next twenty years, to the size of each of our present cities, about as much more again will be added.

Second, along with the concentration into urban areas, there has been another, contrary, tendency for population in each area to spread out away from the central city toward opener land. Again the result of automobile use. In the West, where growth is most rapid, for every new resident of a central city there have been two in the "ring area" of that city. Los Angeles is the most obvious example.

There is another, third movement akin to the second: Those industries, like electronics, which produce lighter, smaller goods, have tended to take themselves away from the cities, away from dependence on railroad transportation, and sit down by the sides of new roads. The same applies to the warehousing and delivery operations of many businesses, since traffic problems are less acute around the perimeter of urban areas.

At the same time that you have watched all this, there have occurred other things, less easily seen from aloft, but which you might infer: an increasing technical, mechanical competence in the population generally, and a tremendous, almost explosive increase, as mentioned, in the amount and variety of materials on which this competence works. The development of plastics is a case in point. An increase in per capita earnings has come, as it should, to those whose incomes before were lowest, along with a leveling of riches generally.

And besides these, take into account those things we have always had: geographical space, and a tremendous store of national wealth.

Now in the most reasonable of worlds, and from where you are sitting, how would you expect that we have provided for ourselves?

Well—since we must get about so much, it follows that our ways of doing it are excellent: our roads wide, spacious, unencumbered by intersections or the remains of over-agile motorists, our public transportation—trains, buses, subways—swift, comfortable, uncrowded, even downright luxurious.

Since, with our moving together, the concerns of different individuals interpenetrate so deeply, and since the way land is used in any one community so much affects the uses and economics of the next, it follows that the location of industries, the building of roads or houses, the marking off of some areas as natural preserves—such things as these are guided by regulatory bodies who represent the interests of many communities, and whose loyalties are not local but regional.

With dispersion, both industrial and personal, *away* from the middle of cities, to areas less crowded, it follows that we have made generous use of land to surround our apartment buildings and houses. An acre or two for each house lot; expansive and private space for trees and gardens, for grace of living, for children to play in with safety.

And our houses themselves? In view of our technical skills, our resources, and the proximity of different crafts, it is only natural that we make houses easily, to suit our various tastes and pocketbooks, with a good one for each of us. With the increase in per capita income, it follows that a private country home is within the reach of everyone who wants it. We make our houses as we make quantity things best—by machine. And make them variously, and adventurously, and beautifully. Some are borne up, like bubbles, by the normal pressure of air inside. Others are built in folding sections, around utility cores—made demountable—to be picked up and moved, as populations move, from one area of the country to another. Some are fabricated on site by concrete techniques. Some are molded from ordinary earth and solidified with plastic additives. Others, still, arrive by truck, as panels, in different stages of pre-assembly, and are slipped or fastened together in a matter of hours. Given wealth of choice and wealth of land, the country worker journeys home to greater comfort than that enjoyed by a plantation owner.

And the centers of cities? They serve an ageless function as social, cultural, and commercial centers—but serve it now without confusion or exclusion. Slums and delinquency have vanished, as have the gaunt, perpendicular "housing projects" of yore. There are no traffic problems, because traffic now stays outside. The retail shopper leaves his car in peripheral areas, and goes by public conveyance—or, by golly, on foot—through stately plazas, through urban meadows garlanded by flowers. The nightingale sings above the hatshop, the voice of the turtle echoes through sunny marble valleys.

Only it isn't exactly that way . . . exactly or at all. . . .

In our general progression of skills, building somehow lags far behind. Not fifty years behind, perhaps—but not much less, at that. It goes still by hammer and handsaw—agonizingly slow, inefficient, and more wasteful of money and people than we can any longer afford. The greatest irony of all is that it is so set about by habit, prejudice, false enthusiasms, and obsolete local constrictions that in a land of free enterprise the look of our urban landscapes is as comfortless, imitative, and repetitive, often, as any dictator could wish.

We descend on the countryside, gouge down hills and level trees, carve our fields into square plots, and set our little houses at right-dress—imitation Cape Cod Colonial mission-type rambling ranch salt boxes, with handkerchief lawns and picture windows facing the highways, with brief veneers of brick and clapboard for variety, and each with its "sales feature": parquet floors, or built-in flower holders, or faucets that whistle *Dixie*. The builder shuffles away. The town struggles to provide new schools. Cities, deprived of income, fight states for their share of tax money. Industry grunts and looks the other way.

A single house consists of about thirty thousand separate pieces, hand-assembled on site—with time out for bad weather. It consumes up to fifteen man-years of work from raw material to completion. A conventional wall—studs, rough boarding, and clapboard—contains the equivalent of two and a half inches of solid wood throughout and costs about seventy-five cents a foot. And of this wood, 34 per cent of the raw material has been wasted in conversion to lumber, and another 20 per cent lost on the job in odd ends and sawdust. For every wall built, another is spilled away, and in every wall built, there is material—properly converted—to build three to ten other, better walls.

One third of a nation, as we are fond of saying, remains ill housed. That does not include those who are ill housed in new houses. The building industry, at full peak of over a million starts a year, can just provide for the new families created in that year, plus those who live "doubled up," without doing anything to replace dwellings already "substandard": needing major repairs, or inside plumbing. Cities, whose centers are clogged and blighted, make brave but futile efforts to provide new housing—but to provide it still within their limits, so as not to lose the wealth of residents. One community dumps its waste into the river; another, downstream, spends millions to clear it out.

Now, for all this, who or what is to blame? Builders, land developers? But theirs is a business with a long history of disaster. Why should they build better houses than the public is able to demand? Especially when their livelihood is at stake. Town building authorities, and the fearful confusion of local codes? But in most cases these represent communities which didn't particularly invite, in fact don't want, new residents. And the codes are strictly written, and enforced just often enough to discourage fly-by-night entrepreneurs—and only incidentally those who want to put up "strange-looking" houses. Architects themselves? But architects, as noted, have directly to do with only 15 per cent of the new houses each year. The profession is in general agreement that the design of small houses is a noble calling—for the other fellow. The regional planners? But until recently no one's asked them to plan anything. They've had to depend on universities for eating money, and try to find some grim satisfaction in predicting inevitabilities. The government? But what do you want anyway, Bud, the government asks—a planned economy?

History is to blame, as much as anything—the mere fact that geographical and administrative boundaries are the product of past centuries, and yet have endured into a time when the activities of few citizens are enclosed by them. This is the machine age, and it is characteristic of machines that they carry our results further and further at the same time that they obscure our view of them.

Take the Boston area as one of many examples: Boston proper, with a population of 809,000, must try to carry the big-city burdens for a metropolitan area of 2,500,000, and 2 per cent of the city area must provide for the deficit of all the rest. Here is one of the severest economic headaches in the country: a tax rate twice that of New York City, itself no Eden, and the steady loss of business and skilled labor to sunnier climes. What, in this situation, would seem more likely than an exchange of information, planning, and cooperation, on a regional level? But the forty different communities of major Boston remain demurely separate, hedged off by unconcern, mistrust, and habit. There is one agency only—the Metropolitan District Commission—whose concerns are permitted to override local interests. And its concerns are sharply limited.

The Boston situation is one of many; the problem is national. Yet there are signs that the problem has begun slowly, painfully, partially to be solved. The increase in private home ownership can be taken as one improvement, and the fact that more private homes are already owned in this country than in any other. The loosening of mortgage restrictions is another, going back to the thirties. A gradual increase in the average size of building lots. The ability, already mentioned, of factories to decentralize. (Since 1940 less than a third of new plants have gone up in cities of over a hundred thousand; before then, over half.) The creation, in a few cities, of special commissions of wide scope—port authorities and the like —which have not much to do with land use, in some cases, but are increasingly drawn toward it. The fact that some cities—Pittsburgh, Philadelphia, Detroit, Cincinnati—are beginning to meet their land and planning problems head on. Lastly, and most general, the popular acceptance of "modern" or "contemporary" architecture, which is as prone to debasement as any other period style, but, to some extent, befits our times.

Since the main interest of this book is the single house and its immediate surroundings, the larger issues just mentioned should be understood as "context" and will figure later on only when they have a special, direct relevance. But concerning regional planning generally, I should like to make one point: that things have happened and will happen to us and to the way we live whether we plan them or not, and it is better to have them happen well—by design —than badly, inevitably, by accident. Regional plans will come because they must. It is only to be hoped that they will develop naturally, reasonably, within our native tradition of doing things. That is, without loss of individuality, self-determination, and popular participation in the making of decisions.

Large programs aside, there remains much to be done on a local or private level. The opportunities which lie open range all the way from, simply, the intelligent choice of an individual house through the reform of building codes, to participation in the founding of small new communities, to (possibly) the assumption of wider responsibilities by industries and private foundations. Any or all of these can go forward in the name of self-interest, and this is perhaps the best reason to hope that forward is the direction in which they will go.

2   Women, People, and Houses

Now women, after all, own most of the property in the United States, elect the President, choose the houses, and, as I understand it, bear most of the children. I remember one occasion when, impressed by these facts and addressing a women's club, I endeavored to draw the attention of my audience to some of the large issues already suggested: our arrival through history to a profoundly new era, the characteristics of the machine age as I think they apply to the business of house design, the complex relationship of family to community, and so on. At the end of it all, the chairlady rose to her feet and said, "Thank you very much, Mr. Koch, for your lovely speech, and I know we will long remember that part about the Thermopane."

On another such occasion, I was a member of a mixed panel of professionals—a real estate salesman, a mortgage banker, a city planner, etc.—and I was asked the question: What did I think a woman wanted in a house? Dignity, I said. A woman is central to her family. The equipment of a house, and its rooms, and the land around it, should be so disposed as to exemplify her role: to make easy her routine chores; to require little of, but offer much to, her instinctive virtues as artist, decorator, and nest-maker; and to encourage her use of leisure time in ways rewarding to herself and useful to her community. I remember the soft intake of breath, the noddings of heads by the ladies present.

And after *that* discussion was over, the real-estate salesman sidled up to me and, removing his cigar, said, "Koch, I didn't want to say anything in front of those others. But you know what a woman *really* wants in a house? She wants a cute little brick terrace—you know, like the one she just saw outside her cousin Aggie's house, that married that rich slob from Buffalo. Or maybe it's a kitchen sink with the curved aluminum splash board. Or a cobbler's bench. Or a bathroom wall with those big, googy blue plastic tiles on it. You show her something like that to look at, you can sell a place with a sod roof, clay floor, and an outside well."

And in a way he spoke the truth. We, all of us—women and men alike—are prey to first impressions. The good salesman of houses will make sure that the hedge is clipped, the lawn is green and smooth. These are what his customers see, getting out of the car. And the white paint on the porch railing, the vase in the vestibule, and the sliding closet door—the one that works. The husband in the party may drum on the walls, or ask a few questions about the hot-water heater, to show that he's the penetrating sort, not deceived by appearances. But it's the little lady who casts the deciding vote. She marches into the kitchen, and is entranced by the grandeur of the spigot. She may pay some passing attention to the relation of stove to sink to counter area, to the number of steps she will have to take to get a meal, or to cabinet space. But not so very much. Neither husband nor wife will ponder long over the arrangement of rooms, the way family and guests will circulate among them, or especially the different needs they must serve in different years of the family's development. Nor will they think much about the land outside: the amount of space their children have to run in, the amount of traffic there is to imperil them, the number of trees available to be climbed, or the orientation of house to sun! And matters at least as important as all these others: the shape of the neighborhood, the possibility of its being encroached upon, the distance to shopping, the quality of schools, the taste of the air—these things, as often as not, are taken on faith or forgotten.

As the continuing satisfaction and value of an individual house, whether built or bought, comes to depend more and more on the things *surrounding* it—land, neighborhood, and community—it follows that the choice of a house becomes an increasingly technical and diverse business, and that the chooser must try to make order of influences which it is difficult to understand and impossible directly to see. For the chooser this is too bad. But for anyone who wants to retain effective control over the way he is housed, there are no convenient alternatives. And if it is women who buy houses, it is women who are going to have to do the understanding.

Certainly there is a tremendous lay interest in things architectural; the success of the home magazine attests to that. And there has been what seems to most designers an improvement in "taste" over the period of the last twenty years. An acceptance of "modern"—the displacement of the porte-cochere by the picture window—and a somewhat formless concern with issues of town planning. Leaving aside the many particular ills of this educative process, it is an encouraging thing.

There remains the peril that our technical development and our economic needs will yet outrace our awareness of them, that architects and planners will be found without good answers to what has to be done, that it will be done any way, and that the results will be distressful for generations.

The mass building of houses has offered clear competitive advantages for some time. The outright prefabrication of houses is beginning to. It is quite likely that prefabrication will arrive, on a large scale, before we are practically and aesthetically "ready," that prefabricated houses will be designed, huckstered, and sold, not for the advantages they can offer, but on the basis of what people are used to, prejudiced in favor of, or can be titillated by: the shape of door handles or the windows that close by motor. We may come to select our houses with the same splendid innocence with which we choose our automobiles: according to the shape of tail fins, or the number of blondes the advertisement shows wedged in the back seat.

Anxiety on these points may seem premature. After all, prefabrication isn't here yet. But it isn't difficult to find instances of popular sentiment which are of little concern to the custom architect, but which, if not "thought out," will bear hard on the course taken by prefabricators. One of them, worth dwelling on, is the question of variety or "individuality" among houses.

The desire not to be stereotyped is legitimate, of course—not to live in exactly the fashion of the next family. And architecture should implement it. Few sights are less uplifting than a straight line of identical, suburban, small brick castles. It would be pleasant if *every* house could be shaped inch by inch to its site, its family, and their preferences. But that has never been the case; there aren't enough families who can afford it, or enough architects to go around. In any event the composition of families changes over time, and they move from one house to another, nowadays, on the average of once every five years.

The craving for individuality, whether "real" or socially inspired, has come to express itself in curious ways. Since, in the great majority of cases, the house we are living in was built for and bought from someone else, the most individuality it can show is not ours but *his*. Or, more likely, *its*—the house's. It may look a good bit different from every other house on the street, but these are *not* our differences. Those rooms were not laid out to accommodate us and our children, but the hypothetical mass family with which, as a statistic, builder and salesman are familiar, and to which, if we are lucky, we conform. In these circumstances the individuality we have retained is that of the hermit crab in another creature's shell—fearful and obsessive.

And yet, economical building is coming to depend more and more on standardized and—not to blink the fact—repetitive elements. This is already the case with conventional construction. How to respond to the fact? The reaction of the conventional builder has already been noted: to build his houses in a neat, close row, add a dormer here, a front stoop there, change the slopes of roof, alternate shingles with siding with clapboard, and hope unsuccessfully that the differences will be convincing. "The monotony of slight variation," as it is often, aptly, called.

It remains to be seen whether the prefabricators will do better (and whether the public will permit them to); whether they will think out the business of repetition and variety; separate the valid considerations from the presumed; strive for variety where it *counts* (inside the house as much as out, and in the living activities to which it serves as context); and achieve variety, not in spite of the standardization of components, but by way of it.

That they are trying is evidenced by the fact that prefabbers reported a total of 238 actively selling models at the end of 1956. The largest prefabricator advertises four different styles of architecture and eighty different floor plans.

Individuality, in the last analysis, should not depend on cupolas; it belongs to people. It is not much buttressed by ornamental rainspouts. The housewife who is aware that her inside living-room wall somewhat resembles her neighbor's can bestir herself to put her own

---

paint or paintings or fabrics on it. The likeness of walls may have helped her toward ten extra feet of space—in the long run, more useful. Her children, outside the house, will be better off with an extra half acre of land than a full set of Colonial shutters. It is in the land, in fact—even in a community of houses alike—that many of the answers lie: in the different ways of orienting a house on its lot, at different distances from the street; with the addition in different fashions of carports, covered walkways, fences, terraces, and planting; and with care to preserve and add to the natural growth of trees. These, as much as anything, vary the profile of a house and give it different emphases. And a family with a fixed amount of money to spend is well advised to put relatively more of it in land and less in house than custom suggests. (In this respect, things *are* improving. The average size of building lots has increased tremendously in many areas during the past decade.)

But even if, let's assume, we plan a community without abundance of land, it may yet be that the looks of it will be satisfying, that it will be a rewarding and useful place to live. It is possible that a good deal more depends, aesthetically, on the arrangement of houses with respect to each other, the intelligence and simplicity of their visible design—without bravura—than on screened-in breezeways. Nature itself is beautiful, or so we like to claim, and nature is not afraid of repetition in the construction of plants and bodies. "It's all a question of how it's done." Nature does it well. The designer may or may not, but he makes a poor start if he only aims at something not done before.

But, in surprising fact, prefabrication will likely afford more meaningful variation than we have had in recent years among houses traditionally built. The house fabricated as a single unit, incapable of modification, will be the exception. Most prefabricated houses will be "modular"—designed, that is, in multiples of certain dimensions, so that one element may be exchanged for another of like size: wall panel for window, or door and frame for wall—and that these modules may be combined into a great number of shapes and spaces. Modularization can be applied most obviously to the framing or "shells" of houses, permitting extensions of length; displacements of space, at right angles or to either side; variation of window pattern; and so on. But a formidable number of things are capable of modularization: closets, cabinets, furniture (already a quantity item), appliances, even bathrooms.

What is profoundly significant, I think, about modular design is how greatly it may increase the opportunity of individual families to interest themselves in, and govern, the planning of their own houses. I can imagine the time—not too far distant—when husband and wife may sit down with a catalog list of house parts and a boxful of model blocks, and lay out rooms and walls exactly to please themselves, doors and windows where they want them, space for furniture, closets, and kitchens. Admittedly their building blocks will represent standardized, mass-produced elements of houses. But if they think their way carefully through their own family requirements, the house itself should be as different from every other as they are from every other family. At a point, obviously, their block building will

The Japanese house (*Museum of Modern Art*)
is a classic example
of modular construction

profit from the attentions of a combination architect-builder-dealer. But their chance to plan for themselves will reach far beyond today's architect-client relationship. They will also have a markedly more exact idea, in advance, of just how much it will cost them to build, and they will have reason for confidence in the beauty of what they have planned—because the modular elements in question will have been designed to relate successfully to each other in an infinite variety of combinations. If we, as house buyers, really mean what we say about our desire to participate in the building of our houses, here, it strikes me, is the best practical opportunity for it since the days of Rameses.

Modular building and planning is nothing new. The Japanese, as one example, have been at it for centuries. (Curious, in a culture so braced by tradition and conservatism.) The size of the modules in the case of the Japanese house is determined by the dimensions of the frame on which the mats are woven. In our country, a number of agencies, such as the American Standards Association, have stood sponsor to the development of modularization, and there is considerable basis of agreement within the building industry as to what constitutes "good" and useful modules. (For one reason or another, four inches, forty inches, and four feet have worked out to be "good" modules for most materials.)

Modular design and modular building tend to look like what they are—right-angular and "paneled." There are those whose sensitivities are pinched by the modular look; I am not one of them. "Colonial" has a look; so does Romanesque, and it may be that, to the

architect in ages to come, "Twentieth-Century Modular" will stand for just as many pleasant, useful, and beautiful things. And with luck, it will stand for the time when the arrangement of living space was given back to those to whom it properly belongs—the people inside.

But the prefabricated house, modular or not, will require a vastly greater degree of architecting than the conventional house, in both components and totality. In what manner may the architect participate?

I think, though it is a difficult thought to express, that as he moves from his traditional "custom" work with individual clients toward designing for volume-building, the architect will feel the stirring of new aesthetic imperatives. I have found this true, at any rate, for myself. My main livelihood for years has come from custom architecture: the planning of single houses, schools, libraries, and the like. But when I sit down to draw for prefabrication, I feel a subtle, personal shifting of gears. Modern architecture, for years—even the best of it—has tended to be a little theatrical, a little showy. Whatever the disclaimers, it retains some elements of façadism. Architects tend still to work in patterns, in surface, not depth, to design what looks well on paper (and wins prizes) and catches attention. This is well and good, even desirable, in the single house. But in the house that is to be built many times over, the dramatic detail may have to yield to something less glamorous, less artful perhaps, and more livable. In this respect I think we should yet take some lessons from the Scandinavians. If I were to select my favorite early examples of this unpretentious, thoughtful architectural spirit, they would be—are—the Collective House by Sven Markelius in Stockholm, Sweden; the Asplund Crematorium near there; and a church by Eric Bryggman in Helsinki, Finland.

If the architect responds thoughtfully to the fact that he is designing for volume, he will become less concerned with his own virtuosity and more with the possibility of permitting his clients and customers to exercise *theirs*. He will give less thought, perhaps, to the misty demands of art, and more to the day-by-day living which will have to go forward in the spaces he has helped to create. He will be more interested in providing the widest possible range of useful, understandable alternatives for the choice—the participation—of the buyer, than in agitating for the "finish" or "complete realization" of his design in any one house. And the houses, or parts of them, which he designs will not proclaim his own particular handhold on beauty, but will aim at unobtrusiveness, adaptability, and—anonymity. Architecture may well be less bold, in order that the living inside it be bolder. The *house* is not the "thing"; it is meant to serve *us*.

It is bewildering to me that nowadays, after the architect has finished weaving his way about us, we then—if we can afford it—hire an interior decorator to tie the final knots. This is our final assertion that we are not only bereft of taste or confidence in visual matters; we have really nothing particular to contribute, from our own way of living, to the spaces that most immediately surround us. Yet I hazard a guess that any woman, untutored by magazines, in a room so designed as to make few demands in itself, will discover herself remarkably conversant with questions of grace and utility, may learn to take pleasure not in how much furniture she can load into that room but how much she can leave out, and do remarkable and pleasing things out of her own family experience—the most recent trip to the seashore, and the finger paintings of the kids.

I persist in believing that a woman *does* want dignity in her house, as in all aspects of her living. Her *own* dignity—not someone else's. Concerns of housing—architecture in the widest sense—are basically relevant to this need, as they are, to take a less engaging example, to problems of juvenile delinquency. At the same time, just as adequate housing at most provides a context in which good juvenile behavior is easily encouraged, so for the woman a good house becomes as much better as she makes it. A great deal of literature has been devoted recently to the spiritual and temporal difficulties of her sex (and not quite so much to the troubles of the male who heightens his blood pressure and shortens his life while providing her with nesting materials). Her solution to them, it would seem, does not consist in a migration from house to house, and most emphatically not in the discovery of new splash boards, terraces, and coffee tables. Or in the proliferation of "labor-saving" gadgets.

But gadgetry may yet take her along the right path. It manifests, in a way, an American striving toward dignity—though to the European the striving may seem materialistic, or just plain sentimental. It is part of a commitment to technical progress. And if this commitment has led us into disappointments, and if it does not, by itself, insure the good life, it may nevertheless have brought us closer to it than the sophisticated will admit. The woman in search of dignity may do worse than inform herself, not only on the feminine and decorative, but the mundane, traditionally masculine details of house construction. Not —as the home magazines are forced to have it—the way a used banjo can be hand-painted into a wall ornament, but rather the art of sills, plates, ledgers, and grouts. Her interests should range ahead in time and outward in space, away from fetching, decorative particulars to the *use* she and her family will make of living spaces and community. Because, whether or not she can hammer a nail, if houses are her business, so specifically is the making of them.

3 Working Toward the Industrial House

The "secrets" of prefabrication are simply those of technology in general: the replacement of hand by machine labor; the advantages this offers in volume, quality control, and economy; the ability to produce and handle in large physical sizes and to gather and distribute over wide geographical areas. Every house is to some extent prefabricated—by virtue of glass, wallboard, washing machine and the like. And every attempt at an exact definition of prefabrication resolves to the confession, finally, that it's all a matter of degree, consisting in the amount of labor, material, and expense that go toward completing a house *before* in comparison to *after* its arrival at the building site.

The logic of machine use is familiar, comfortable, and undeniable. The effort to apply it thoroughly and meaningfully to the edgy, noisy, particular business of house making is something else again. It may be helpful to summarize the history of a few of the influences leading toward the industrial house, and then—by way of making clear some of the difficulties involved—to examine the circumstances of a typical, hypothetical, present-day producer.

If we look for the beginnings of prefabrication, as Burnham Kelly has noted, we are led back not several dozen but several thousands of years. (The Mesopotamians made crude clay bricks. And a brick is not only a prefabricated material, but "modular" as well.) And there have been temporary booms of the industry even previous to this century, as in the

California Gold Rush. But it is in the last fifty years that it has counted for anything, beginning with the mass marketing of the pre-cut, wood-frame house.

The pre-cut house represents the simplest practical aspect of prefabrication. It comes essentially as a bundle of pieces to be assembled by buyer or contractor into a shell, with most details of finish, plumbing, etc., left to his later discretion. From the turn of the century to now, the pre-cut house has sold in volume. In this country, over a quarter of a million have been set up.

Around 1900, too, there developed an interest in concrete—not merely as a foundation material, but for use in slab floors and walls and ceilings. Grosvenor Atterbury was one of the pioneers of concrete construction (another was Thomas Edison). And experiment continues to this day with the development of lightweight aggregates and "foams," and with site-fabrication techniques like that of the Neff Airform House—cement sprayed over inflated rubber forms—and contrivances like H. G. LeTourneau's mammoth "Tournalayer," which sets out whole houses like eggs. So far, however, for small-house construction, the charms of concrete have tended to be offset by the expense and equipment required to heave it about.

Steel as a material for prefabrication came into favor in Britain, after the first World War, when there was a great surplus of it. The first steel houses, unfortunately, were literal imitations of traditional houses in brick, ignoring the special virtues and shortcomings of the metal, and most of them rusted vigorously away. (Since then, of course, we've learned to use

---

it better. Metals continue to hold great promise—aluminum and magnesium, besides steel —along with combinations of metal and enamel, as in the Lustron house.)

The Germans explored a number of other materials besides steel and cement, and were active in the development of modular apartment houses until, in 1933, the Nazis decided that this sort of thing was unworthy of the national heritage, and diverted the materials to military purposes.

The Swedes and other Scandinavians, meanwhile, had begun to prefabricate in wood, of which they had an abundance, and did themselves proud. (My own introduction to pre-fabrication, in fact, came in Sweden in 1938, while I was abroad on a fellowship. I remember being somewhat intrigued by the do-it-yourself aspects of the thing—families working on weekends to put together wood-panel walls, and roofs on walls—but at the time it didn't seem to me like the sort of thing a "real" architect should concern himself with.)

In the United States there were few developments before the thirties, except for the research of Albert Farwell Bemis, and the unabashed experimentation of designers like Buckminster Fuller. Bemis, through Bemis Industries, Inc., explored a number of materials and construction techniques, and developed the "cubical modular" method of design, by way of urging the industrial standardization of components, and illustrating the limitless variety of plans available from them. Fuller, with the Dymaxion house, brought about the first forcible introduction of many people to "crazy" architecture. (Frank Lloyd Wright was

DYMAXION

TYPE Suspension
SPONSOR R. Buckminster Fuller
COUNTRY United States

DATE-1928

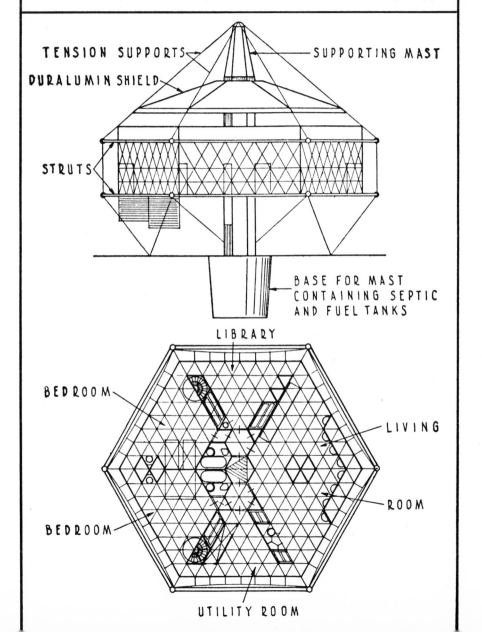

TENSION SUPPORTS → ← SUPPORTING MAST

DURALUMIN SHIELD

STRUTS

BASE FOR MAST CONTAINING SEPTIC AND FUEL TANKS

LIBRARY

BEDROOM

LIVING

ROOM

BEDROOM

UTILITY ROOM

---

known to be a little tetched, but he at least had never proposed to hang a house in mid-air.)

But it was in the Depression that industrialized housing, if not getting its "start," became at least a topic of national importance. Most general, but most significant, was the change in public climate—a disillusion with traditional ways of doing things and an excitement with new ways (and a commitment then and since to the wonder-working of science). Specific influences have been too numerous to mention but a few: the growth of the housing problem (or awareness of it); the involvement of large companies, in the thirties, in search of commercial outlets; the work of such institutions as the Bureau of Standards, the National Forest Products Laboratory, and the Pierce Foundation; and the personal and professional influence of architects responsive to the promises of the age such as Fisher, Wagner, Willson, Gropius, Neutra, Nelson, Atwood, Fuller, Keck, and many, many others.

As to the extent and methods of prefabrication: In this country, typically, these have varied widely from producer to producer. If we take the pre-cut house to represent the most elementary conception, then the ultimate, presumably, would be the house which arrives on site—any site—all in one lump, requires no attachment to permanent foundations or to external water, power, or sewage facilities, and can be packed up and moved at a moment's notice. This is not entirely fanciful; the Acorn House, in some respects, is a close approach. But the inventive in-betweens are and have been numerous. For instance: systems of transporting and bolting together houses from completed sections (Pressed Steel Car Company);

adaptations from trailer design (TVA, and Transa-Housing, Inc.); and the Wagner Steel "igloo"; the Fuller "Grain Bin" houses, and such site-pouring concrete methods as those of the Ibec Corporation. One should also add the routinized labor-saving methods of such large-operative builders as the Levitts, which, if not prefabrication in the strict sense, take advantage of the same economics.

It is in the past ten years, particularly in the last five, that prefabrication has begun to take a meaningful cut at the housing pie. Indications of the trend appear conclusive.

Leaving aside pre-cut houses, and the large builders—who don't belong and are glad of it—we find that the total output of prefabricated dwellings between 1935 and 1940 was about ten thousand—something less than 1 per cent of all houses built. Between 1946 and 1956, the total had risen to about half a million units, an average of about 5 per cent a year. In 1956, ninety-four thousand—10 per cent. There are about three hundred firms of all sizes in the field. Of these the "giants" are National, Pease, Harnischfeger, U.S. Steel Homes, American Homes, Scholz, and Techbuilt (a giant of small size).

But 10 per cent is still a far cry from 90 per cent. It's reasonable to ask why the capacities of mass production in almost every other field have outstripped the rise of living costs, and yet in housing have lagged so far behind. And if, as I've made bold to say, the industrialized house is inevitable, why is it taking so long to happen?

A systematic list of reasons would run to some length. And the following general considerations would apply to all: A house is perhaps the largest, most complicated, expensive, and *personal* of all consumer products. Correspondingly, it is one of the most difficult to organize onto an orderly volume-production basis. Besides the usual problems of machine use, capital investment, and overhead, the prefabricator faces innumerable "outside" difficulties: distribution and dealership; the "commitedness" of a volume product in relation to fluctuating public acceptance; the weight of local customs and legalities—a thousand and one obscure hazards, of which any one, at any time, may become critically important. So it is that the broad direction of our economic and technical development, however clearly we see it, may have remarkably little bearing on the efforts of an individual small producer to keep from going broke.

Let's take one such—call him Charlie—and consider how he operates, how he would *like* to operate, and what holds him back. (The case is fictitious.)

Charlie began as a carpenter and successful small builder. His decision to take his work indoors—to industrialize—arose from two motives: In the first place, he had trouble finding, and keeping, other good carpenters, and it occurred to him that he could use machinery to replace the precision that a craftsman has by instinct; in the second place, he was tired of the rain running down his neck.

Charlie cleaned out a shed and began to make up the side walls of his houses in sections, as "frame panels." (In effect, a frame panel is what you get if you make vertical cuts, at intervals, of a conventionally framed and boarded wall.) The machinery involved was simple, and so were the design changes he made to accommodate this element of modularity to the kind of houses he had been building right along. He continued to do the rest of his work in the field, and to change the size of his frame panels according to the house in question. Until the day when—seeing how much time he saved in his framing (cutting his studs, for instance, in one continuous operation); and thinking how much *more* time he could save by prefabbing other parts of the house such as closets, floors, even roofs; and knowing where he could get a good buy on a nailing machine—Charlie drew in his breath and made the plunge.

At first sight, it wasn't a very deep plunge, and Charlie would appear to have prospered. Today he does business over a hundred-mile area. He has a "plant" (mostly roof, in fact, sheltering a number of woodworking machines) and a small, permanent labor force. He markets four different basic houses, conventional in appearance, with a judicious salting of "modern" features and trim details—cupolas, porches, and the like. Model III, the "Ranch," is the big seller at present, but model II, the "Cape," is coming back strong. He makes them, still, out of frame panels (it vexes him that he's never been able to make the panels fully interchangeable from one house to another). He uses more plywood than he used to (tough, light, easy to store, and available in quantity), and he prefabricates floors, roofs, closets, doors, stairs, and cabinets, as well as walls. He delivers his panels by truck.

Erection, exterior and interior finishing, and cabinetry are done by crews on the site. Foundation work, wiring, plumbing, heating installation, and the like are done by local outfits—he furnishes plans which they ignore. Whenever he can, he builds the houses in groups of four or five by arrangement with some land developer. He finds now that to keep his plant busy, he must sell his house "packages" to other builders to put up and sell themselves.

But it sometimes seems to Charlie that he has only succeeded in adding all the headaches of a plant manager—cost accounting, maintenance, personnel, and machinery and storage—to the troubles he started with. He does a big business, to be sure, but he has to, just to break even. He has two salesmen on the road for him; they seem to spend most of their time just driving around the countryside at his expense. He has big trucking costs. He has problems with his schedule of work—especially during the winter, when everyone is either working overtime or sitting around with nothing to do. He hesitates to build houses ahead of orders—a house is a bulky, expensive thing to stockpile—or he could keep things busier. And in his sour moments he finds fault with the houses themselves.

The houses are good ones, better in fact than he used to make: stronger, tighter, and better finished. They don't have a "prefabricated look." But somehow, in spite of the speed with which he can make them, they don't cost much less than a conventional house when they're all done. And they should; he knows they should. And if they did, he could sell more of them. As it is, Charlie makes a go of it. And last year a real university asked him to a housing conference. But in his heart of hearts he feels he should be making *more* than a go. Why isn't he?

For one thing, the fact is that he doesn't—can't—prefabricate *enough;* what he has done, mainly, is to move indoors and systematize the routine carpentry work on the "shell" of routine houses. And the shell of the present-day house—its visible surface—represents as little as one quarter of its total cost. Fifty years ago, it would have been closer to one half, a hundred years ago close to all. But in that lapse of time we have moved indoors, or radically improved the "services" of the house: laundering, bathrooming, heating, food preservation, lighting. (A course on architecture which was wholly rationalized in terms of expense would have to concern itself less with Gropius and Pierre L'Enfant than with the aesthetics of plumbing trees.) So that even an appreciable saving in shell construction will have little bearing on the total cost of the house.

Then there is the fact that Charlie, building houses deliberately conventional in appearance, is using factory methods to imitate a handicraft product. This can surely be done —the Grecian Urn Water Closet, I suppose, is the classic example—but it is by now a familiar axiom that efficient machine use implies changes in the appearance of useful things.

None of this is news to Charlie. He knows he could, or should, prefabricate more than the shell. He is aware of different techniques in wood construction and, for that matter, of other materials besides wood—the metals, or even paper and plastics. He's tempted often to hire an architect to rethink all his designs, mash down his direct production costs, to do by machine all that machines do best, and offer a more complete package—a house which, even if its appearance is a little extreme, is irresistible in its good sense and low cost. A service to humanity. He likes the idea; what keeps him from it?

First of all, the money. He has a lot of it tied up already. He is hesitant to junk a process which works, after all, and put himself deliberately in the position of starting from scratch, especially when capital, in this field, is so immensely hard to come by. And yet he might risk it, make his production process more complex, more remote from the building of individual houses on individual sites, sink funds in new machinery and hope to earn it back over a long period—*if* he could count on a steady, specific public demand. But he can't. True, there is a chronic need for housing. But to him, as a supplier, it has always come as feast or famine. He will be entering an untried product into competition with regular builders, and with all houses already built. To his prospective customers, the transaction of house getting is one of the most important they can make, laden with sentiments which reach back beyond their childhood to the atavistic past. Their ability to say "No" is as limber where a fifteen-thousand-dollar house is concerned as it is with a twenty-cent mousetrap.

And *still* Charlie might risk it—if the complications ended there. But a house is not bought over the counter, and carried around. It goes out, and is attached to the ground, and to public utilities, in a particular location in a particular community. And before it is sold, in most cases, it is mortgaged. It is sold not to a customer but, in effect, to a bank, and by indirection, often to the Federal government. And in all this, the opportunities for discomfort are practically unlimited.

Take, as one example, the matter of mortgage approval and the workings of the FHA. To Charlie, the FHA is a mixed blessing. As an agency it is conservatively administered. It endeavors to support high standards of construction. But in its local administration, the rules and rules of thumb are almost invariably those of standard practice. More than one prefabricated house has been approved by FHA at the national level, and disapproved at the local, on the grounds that it is unfamiliar—and therefore its resalability is questionable. That the houses *do* resell, and usually at a profit, may sway no one at all.

Or take the matter of local antipathies. A house produced at a distance, coming into a community, unsettles local perquisites and is certain to arouse a degree of instinctive opposition from local builders, suppliers, *rentiers,* local trades unions, and groups of residents —particularly if it comes in a "development." (It should be noted that the attitude of labor unions on the national level toward prefabrication has been remarkably good—but, as in the case of the FHA, this can have surprisingly little influence on local functionaries.) This is the reason, for instance, that Charlie makes no effort to prefabricate a piping or "utilities" core—the plumbers would murder him.

Last of all comes the matter of building codes. These, properly, are a chapter unto themselves or even a book which badly needs writing. I can only hope to describe a few of their virtues and fine-grinding limitations.

Most towns have building codes. They represent a healthy reaction from the time when people built as they pleased, and often very badly. They have the force of law, but are seldom the work of lawyers. They are administered by building inspectors, usually political appointees on a part-time basis, whose salaries are low, whose own professional interests are often involved, and whose abilities and integrity vary from the excellent to the abysmal. The code of any one town is likely to differ in fundamental respects from the code of the next. (As fundamental, indeed, as the listed "fiber stress" of woods—a measure of their internal strength.) The difference between one code and the next may be as obvious as the fact that one town prohibits the "slab" house, without basement—and the next will permit a basement only if it has a plastered ceiling. Or it will extend to costly minutiae of wiring, or the distances at which particular kinds of venting may be located from plumbing traps. (It may be admitted, out-of-hand, that legitimate issues of safety and health *are* involved, and that each town is entitled to its own opinion of what is safe and healthy, but it is possible that there is an objective basis for agreement on some of these things.) The implications of it all for Charlie the prefabricator are obvious. The more complete the house he offers, the more certain he is of having to rip out installed wires and pipes, fur out walls, add fictitious fire stops to the bottom step of open stairways, change dimensions of sills—do a number of things which, at best, add nothing to the soundness of his construction, cost from hundreds to thousands of dollars in labor and delay, and serve only to bring the house into a specious conformity with those around it.

The provisions of a given code will date back from one to several score years. They are usually compatible with each other—not always—and seldom require, though often permit, practices which are clearly unsound. They often preclude the use of methods and materials alternative or superior to those which were customary at the time the code was written. Many plumbing codes in the Midwest, for example, written in the days of cast iron, will not permit the use of copper piping, which is better in almost all practical respects. They often make curious omissions, such as specifying that all floor joists shall be 2 by 10 inches, and then neglecting to mention the distances these joists shall be allowed to span. (A 2 by 10 spanning fifteen feet is less than one half as strong as a 2 by 10 over ten feet.)

Some articles of code—such as the not-infrequent provision that any new building shall conform in appearance to the architectural tradition of the community (usually a heritage from the golden age of Polk and McKinley)—come perilously close to an infringement of individual rights. Especially when they are interpreted by a truculent building inspector with his artistic roots in animal husbandry. Most articles of code don't come to much, one by one. They are only distressing in the aggregate, and downright injurious in combination with, and contradiction of, the code requirements of thousands of other communities.

Most codes, fairly enough, give building inspectors (and fire, wiring, plumbing, and health inspectors) discretion, in some instances, to permit the use of materials and techniques which are provably as adequate as those specified in the written code. Here again arise problems of delay and competence. To conduct engineering tests on the strength of a material can take time. If the results of such a test are already available, they are often so complicated that they require a trained engineer to read them. For the inspector, the safest and least embarrassing course of action is to hew to the letter of the law.

Most codes allow appeals, against specific articles or specific decisions by the inspector, to be made to a board of town officials. The purpose is eminently just. But the paper work and delay involved may effectively ruin a closely planned construction schedule. (Many of the large prefabricators, in fact, make a systematic filing of all protests against the code, for an entire area, some months before they propose to do any building. It works very well, usually —and costs more money than many builders have to start with.) There is the additional concern that if, by appeal, the builder has injured the feelings of his inspector, the latter has fifty or more ways of redressing grievances. The next time a phase of construction is complete —masonwork, say—and awaits approval (and everything else waits on *it*) the inspector may be sick abed, or engaged across town on a three-day tour of a silo.

In recent years there have been many efforts to repair the deficiencies and discrepancies of local codes. One such is the writing of "performance codes," for instance, which do not undertake the endless task of prescribing materials, but instead establish minimum standards for strength of walls, ventilation, sanitary facilities, and the like. Some towns have adopted performance codes, and so have many states.

The Federal government has, through its own housing activities—FHA, Bureau of Standards, and so on—provided a wealth of useful code material which is available to any municipality that wishes to bring itself up to date.

There still remains the problem of administration. The performance code does not offer the building inspector the same safe points of retreat as the routine code; it requires more of him in engineering competence. And there are still problems of delay and expense. The Massachusetts performance code, adopted in 1947, actually contained provisions for appeal from the decisions of a local town direct to state authority. Radical additions to the code led to its being repealed, but during its short life it was able to make several significant changes.

The need for building-code reform has been evident for some time, and little by little the need is being met. There is one thing in particular that makes the going slow. Codes are voted on by (and, if reformed, will have to be reformed by) those who are already residents of towns—those who liked the way the town looked when *they* came to it and built, not the way the town would look after a whole lot of *other* people would come and build, and who have little or no interest in making building requirements easier for the newcomers than they had them for themselves.

So it is that Charlie the prefabricator ranges all these things in his mind—the costs, the uncertain profits, the certain antipathies, the possibility that he will have to take his daughter out of Radcliffe—and decides to leave the job for someone else a lot bigger than he is.

And it's reasonable to wonder why he got into prefabrication to start with—why anyone does. It is an untidy business—its concerns are not properly those of the architect, or the factory manager, or the builder, or the merchandiser. They mush out over all traditional boundaries. Yet year by year more good souls launch themselves into this deadly porridge. And I myself have been immersed in it so long and deeply that I can scarce recall the fair Dorian shores described to me in architectural school.

My first practical involvement with the idea of houses in volume came in 1939, after some years as a custom architect, with the design of a subcommunity of five houses on Snake Hill in Belmont, Massachusetts. Five is not much of a volume, but the experience was enough to suggest some of the economies possible in quantity design. The houses were individual in plan and elevation. They were standardized with respect to windows, exterior boarding, roofing, equipment, cabinet details, and the like. They came out to cost surprisingly little, even for those days: thirty cents per cubic foot. Five thousand dollars bought a three-story

house. The experience also demonstrated the importance of some of the undesignerly, unbuild-erly problems mentioned before, which, as an architect, I had always been happy to leave aside: how, artistically and legally, to divide up the land, bring in electricity and water, seek the indulgence of town officials in putting a road up a hill which nature had made steeper than the law allowed, and so on. The design of the houses themselves had to be compressed into two months' time. The settling of these other details—inconsequential as they might seem from a "creative" point of view—took five times as long.

The Snake Hill houses were not prefabricated. But in 1945, after the war, with Huson Jackson and John Callender, I designed the Acorn House, which *was* prefabricated —or was meant to be. The Acorn, though demure in most visible characteristics, was designed as a revolutionary, rather than evolutionary, approach to the problems I have described earlier in this chapter. With respect to material, strength, manufacturing technique, and ease of distribution and erection, the Acorn offered demonstrable advantages. To matters of local building code, conventional sales appeal, and mortgage financing, it made few if any concessions. With respect to problems of dealership—we never got that far.

After Acorn came a period when Fritz Day and Leon Lipshutz, my associates, and I served as architectural consultants to the Lustron Corporation. Lustron, unlike Acorn, was dedicated to the proposition that "you can't start little." In its bigness Lustron included a number of virtues and a few conclusive ills. And then, after Lustron, came the design of the

Conantum community in Concord, Massachusetts, and then, most recently and significantly, the design and marketing of the Techbuilt house.

Each of these undertakings is summarized later. And each has underscored the importance of one or more of the unarchitectural, unindustrial, unbuilderly, unsalesmanlike concerns mentioned before. A "good" design for prefabrication is not simply a plan for a handsome house, or, on the other hand, for a handsome mechanical routine, but an all-inclusive, front-to-back affair.

4 The Designer and His Kicks

As the Puritans came wading ashore on the meager coasts of New England, it may be that they looked far ahead to the new civilization. But as they stood vibrating in the keen local breezes, they developed an immediate practical interest in getting warm. In some localities they spent their first winters underground, burrowed in the earth of hillsides. In later years, above ground, they built houses which centered around immense fireplace-ovens and admitted the out-of-doors through discreetly small windows, constructed first with paper or skins, and later with a few, precious squares of glass.

Today, we have to admit, the practical need for a fireplace has all but vanished. Fireplaces are inefficient—realizing about five per cent of the heating value of their fuel—messy, and expensive. Yet we still build them, and sit around rubbing our ankles and thinking comfortable thoughts, like our Puritan ancestors and their chattering, neolithic forebears. (I must confess, even, to having designed a *prefabricated* fireplace, for the Acorn House.) And today, with a plenitude of glass and of methods of lighting and heating and ventilation, after an imitative century of building small-paned Colonial windows, we suddenly discover that we can make windows as high and wide as we want. At the same time, uneasily, we discover that there is no irreducible need for a house to have any windows at *all*. (I leave aside the possibility of deep, human, psychological cravings, about which much is talked and little known.)

The house builder today—more especially the architect and designer—flounders in a profusion of choices and materials, caught between what he finds beautiful (or maybe, he reflects, he only finds it so out of habit) and what, though unbeautiful, is mechanically efficient (but maybe something even more efficient will come along)—nervously trying to decide how to fit what to what.

In their privacy and poverty, the ancients had some advantages. Although, as noted, there are not many things a house *has* to be or do, they had to work hard to make it suffice for that—with adobe, sod, straw, logs, or whatever. It was a matter, generally speaking, of clear necessities barely achieved. Today's architect is confronted by an awesome wealth of materials, techniques, and conceptions, and operates in a widely interpenetrated society. What was domestic is increasingly public. The decisions he makes will set up economic and social reverberations far beyond his hearing. Aware of this, he casts about for the necessities to guide his decisions—and his necessities have vanished. Or appear to. The effects on him, professionally and personally, are several.

As one small example: Though he will never admit it, things like building codes, the tradition of hand labor, however wasteful, and restrictive local union practices may be a comfort to him. They narrow the range of things he might have to try to do.

More importantly, he has to try to know more: more kinds of engineering, economics, more about transportation, the properties of more things from subsoil to sliding doors. At the same time, as things have worked out, he is likely to specialize in a given field of architecture, and to collaborate on most projects with other architects. Group thinking—"team-work"—pervades architecture as deeply as any profession. (Of my own seventeen years as a practicing architect, fourteen have been spent in association with others. Few designs during that time, and none of those of which I speak in later chapters, have been mine alone.)

In a more personal way, the architect is likely to insulate himself from uncomfortable thoughts by developing a "style," often a style for its own sake. He develops a stock in trade —a preference, say, for a certain class of materials. He builds a reputation, or one is assigned to him (my own, I grieve to say, is sometimes given as "modern but not *too* modern"). And this, for a while, is solace. But he has a jittery artistic awareness of other styles and changes in fashion, and a timidity of formulae. If a material or a technique threatens to become over-popular or overuseful, he may abandon it. (Thus, in the in-group of architectural publications, we read of "modular thinking stereotypes" and the "hyperbolic paraboloid clichè"— even before the general public has become aware of these at all.) In happy moments, this finicking may appear to the architect as an aspect of the pioneer spirit; at other times, as a dogtrot between watering places.

Confusion welcomes obscurity. He may seek to reinforce practical by aesthetic necessities. And while no one can deny the usefulness—unifying and excitatory—of the architectural ideologies of the last half century, I am not sure that they have been remarkable for their inner consistency. Many appear to do service after the fact.

(Taking, for instance, the spate of theories expressed in terms of "the machine": In practice most of these seem to reduce to the expansive use of certain materials, and the careful building and intersection of planes. All well and good-looking. But I have been struck by the amount of painstaking hand labor and expense—the endless smoothing of plaster walls, or using steel columns as decorative pilasters—often involved in the reach for "machine" simplicities. And solutions of this kind as much represent the characteristics and capacities of this age as a doily under an eggbeater.)

It is discoverable, I think, that in recent years there has been an almost geometric rate of increase in variety of materials. (I take the term in its broadest sense, to include everything from twopenny nails to techniques of conceiving or purposing a house.) Moreover, each material by itself has tended to become more complex, often larger, and in any case more determinative of other things about the house. In some cases the foreseeable implications in the use of different, promising materials are downright contradictory, and will have to be resolved by experiment. As one result of all this: The present confusion of architecture is likely to get worse before it gets better. As another: The future architect, most likely, will have to give over some of his present wide range of efforts, in order to concentrate his abilities more exactly where they are needed.

No one illustration is entirely apt. But it may help to make some points if we consider first some various ways of heating a house from the time of the fireplace to the conjectural future, then the different possible applications of a given class of materials—plastics—and then, in passing, a few of the engaging conceptions of a single designer, Buckminster Fuller.

It took several hundreds of winters for the evolution from the open fireplace to wood and coal stoves to the popular use of furnaces. And we were surprisingly far along in this country before (with gravity hot-water, or "steam," heat) furnace heat was distributed through an intermediary element rather than direct through the air itself by diffusion or convection. But since the 1920's, things have gone a good deal faster. Steam heat was first refined to "vapor" heat—steam at lower pressure and temperature—and then into forced warm-water systems. The hot-air people, fearful of being left behind, adopted the same principle: a more rapid, forced circulation and thereby a lower required temperature in the medium itself—forced warm air. In both cases, to an already elaborate system of furnace, radiators, and duct or pipe work were added motors and blowers and pumps. And the furnaces themselves were specialized in order to make use of fuels like oil and gas as well as coal.

Then, along with the one-story slab house, came radiant heat and a whole new set of mechanisms and requirements. (The technique, as has often been pointed out, was known to the old Romans and Koreans, but they made less bother about it.) With radiant heating the warmth of the circulating medium is transferred to a larger surface—floor or ceiling usually —which itself acts as radiator, at still lower temperature. The first popular radiant systems used hot-water tubing. Again the hot-air people counted themselves in, with new methods of ductwork or plena (the Lustron house used a radiant hot-air system in the ceiling). And the electricity people joined the fray, having, after all, made toasters for years.

Once more the result was a tremendous proliferation of alternatives and equipment: pipes, pumps, wires, fuels, fans, and so on and on. For the architect, this means more complication of choice and more things dependent on the choice he makes. Shall it be radiant? What kind? And floor or ceiling? If floor, should ductwork be included in the poured slabs, or in a hollow-block system—or should the floor itself be raised? What are the relative costs? What kind of floor covering? What effect will the decision have on other elements of construction: framing, shape of rooms, and the schedule of trade work? At the outset of any new development, the architect is often more daring than the engineer (we had to design our own first radiant-heating system). As the systems improve and become more complex, the architect more and more often conveys his problem to the heating engineer—another professional—and asks, "What do you recommend?"

Here, surely, are concerns enough. And concerns of the last thirty years. But we have only just begun. There are combined systems and split systems—like air fanned over steam or coils. There is the recent development of the heat pump, already adequate in mild climates, and there is the work of those researchers who insist, usefully, on asking basic questions about the whole affair.

Why, for instance, burn fuel to get heat, when the sun sends lots of it free? There have been experiments with substances like Glauber's salts, which melt and store up heat when the sun is high, crystallize and release it when the sun is gone. Build a wall of cans of Glauber's salts, devise a way of blanketing it alternately, on one side or the other, and the thing is done. Or so goes the theory. There are still other heat-collecting systems using media closer in properties to water and involving reservoirs, ornate systems of tubing, and black, absorbent surfaces. So far they seem to promise only nuisance—but so did the spinning jenny.

Other experimenters, concerned with the nature of the heating process itself, are much taken with the principle of "reflective heating" (as opposed to heating by transfer or convection). The best analogy is that of a heat "particle" moving at high velocity and spending its energy, not on the surrounding air, but on the body it strikes. It is because of reflected heat that the skier on a bright day, surrounded by snow, may stay comfortably warm, though the measurable temperature of the air surrounding him is below freezing, and though the sun's rays have passed through millions of even more frigid miles. (Radiant heating, already discussed, operates on this same principle—but more in theory than fact.) And the same principle, moved indoors, could lead to arrangements whereby the walls, floors, and ceilings of rooms are surfaced with something on the order of aluminum leaf or metallized plastic—to take the place of the snow field—and electric-panel heat sources are so oriented as to beam against the occupants, both direct and by ricochet. Presumably we would snap on this kind of heat like an electric light, on entering a room, and douse it when we left. Most likely we would discover that this kind of heat works best in particular shapes of room, with particular shapes of wall—or perhaps that we have no need for solid exterior walls, at all, but rather arrangements of metallized fabric on frames which we leave open in fair weather and close against the wind or really cold weather to increase the reflective surfaces.

Reflective heating, presumably, would be saving of fuel even with the present high cost of electricity. But then, in this connection, we should take account of the predictions that, in a relatively few years, atomic power will give us electricity "too cheap to meter." And quite likely there will be applications of atomic or solar energy to problems of heating in ways considerably more direct than those just mentioned.

It doesn't end here. Most recently there has been some stir over "electronic heating," which involves passing direct current through two dissimilar metals joined by electrical contact. Such a system would offer economy of operation and of means, since ducts, fans, central plant, etc., would be eliminated and only wire lead-ins to small units or room panels would be required.

(Of course, to talk about heating at all is a little old-fashioned. In some parts of the country it's of less concern than the problem of staying cool. And the big thing now is what the ad men fondly call "year 'round climate control," which implies yet more cunning methods of humidity control and air cleaning and will keep us as wonderfully separated from nature, and as pure, as laboratory rats.)

Now let's take all of these things together, or rather, affirm that they *can't* be taken together. Some of the systems which now appear likely, *aren't.* Some will prove disadvantageous in comparison with others, or will be applicable only in special climates or as partial solutions, or will offer spectacular comforts at certain stages of our technical development and then, like steam heat, slowly fizzle out. But which and when and in what manner? The architect knows only that he is already perplexed in his choice between systems, that it bears more and more heavily on his choice of construction techniques, and that tomorrow—in his conscientious regard for the latest, best, and most economical solutions—his perplexity will be several times worse.

As a matter of getting along on a day-to-day basis, the working architect can't afford to be too much diverted by the bright, futuristic promises of new techniques. And he may wonder, since he already provides for so much beyond the simple, material satisfaction of shelter requirements, whether he perhaps is providing too *much*. Every once in a while he visits his clients, and they tell him about how much fun they had when the power went off, cooking over the fireplace. But even on a day-to-day basis, he is made aware by manufacturers of the accomplishments of products now in use—glass, processed woods, paper, metals —and if he is trustful of what he reads, it might appear that he could build a whole house from any *one* of them.

Consider the wonders of the plastics industry, developing out of the quest for a resilient billiard ball. The virtues of plastics, to speak in the most general terms, are their formability to complex shapes; lightness, together with strength; their easy combination with other substances (as in impregnation or lamination processes like plywood); and the variety of colors and transparencies (hence decorative or light-control values) in which they can be made. Their disadvantages—in some cases only—are relatively low durability, sensitivity to light and heat, low-dimensional stability in wall surfaces, and poor acoustical and thermal insulation value (as solid materials).

One of the already practicable uses of plastics, not much exploited, is in sandwich-panel combinations. Plastic is used in this case to impregnate and bond the core of the panel, often corrugated paper, to inner and outer sheets—often but not necessarily plywood. What results is a "stressed-skin" construction, the rigid joining of two separated surfaces into a single structural member, with tremendously high strength in relation to weight. The strength comes (the point is worth extending) from the fact that any pressure against the panel is resisted by both the strength-in-tension of one surface and the strength-in-compression of the other, as in a steel I beam. Thus:

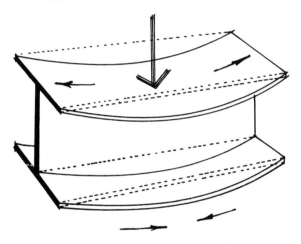

In this way a wall section, say two inches thick by eight by ten feet, light enough to carry around, can do the work of a wood-framed wall three times thicker, four times heavier, and incomparably more wasteful of material.

Another use of plastics is as "foamed cores" to sandwich panels, or even inside conventional walls. Here the use is not structural but insulative—millions of bubbles of dead air space to block the passage of heat. It is conceivable that, within a few years, foaming techniques will replace current methods of insulation, and work important changes in methods of house assembly and jointing. For roofs, it could be, plastics will be sprayed or troweled or rolled on—roofs with the insulation outside. Or, if sufficient strength can be developed, there may be roofs and walls consisting of nothing *but* insulation. There are hints of success with single plastic materials which, like foam rubber, coagulate into smooth surfaces outside and make themselves into their own sandwiches.

Then there are uses of plastics in translucent or transparent sheets, admitting light to interior rooms. There are some doubtful qualities to the material now most used—glass-fiber polyester laminate, under a variety of trade names—but these will improve. And plastic sheeting can be cemented to grids of metal, to make fully structural walls.

Where a wall doesn't have to be structural—and inside a house it often doesn't—it is possible that the size and shape of rooms might be adjusted by walls that fold, slide, or are just plain picked up, moved, and refastened. Such walls, possibly of plastic-impregnated cardboard, would probably never offer much in the way of soundproofing. But noise, as houses go nowadays, is something we may have to get used to.

Uses of plastic with respect to the mechanical elements of the house become increasingly more chancy. But besides the engaging prospect of molded sinks, tubs, and toilets warm to the touch, there is the considerably more important possibility of flexible plastic plumbing. As things now stand, there is no plastic which is sufficiently flexible and resistant to heat and pressure, all at once. But the idea of a pipe less expensive than copper which might be strung to any point in a house is remarkably uplifting to most designers. It might all lead to fixtures which, as well as walls, could be carried around by hand and plugged in where convenient.

But possibly the most bizarre conjecture of all is that of a cheap, plastic "earth stabilizer," which, applied as a spray, would harden to form an elastic membrane to shapes molded out of ordinary soil. Theoretically, at least, walls, chairs, couches, stairways—most anything—could be heaped up by hand into an appropriate shape, and squirted. Every man his own architect—and a large, hard-working family could house itself in a matter of days.

I don't, I confess, hold out great hopes for earth-stabilizing techniques or a number of these other nice things. But if we are willing to believe that plastics can be most everything, we can imagine ourselves a house like *this:*

In some ways it will resemble the crystal palaces we read of in story books but are somehow always done out of. The outer walls will be changeable—clear, translucent, or opaque, depending on the gas or liquid we select to pump through them—and patterned by the structure of the core material itself. The house will probably have a paneled or honeycombed look because this is how the material is best fabricated, and indeed this aspect may be emphasized by striations in the material itself, and by gaskets or taping at the joints. If inner space is to be arrangeable, this suggests that utilities will be located in a central "core" arrangement (though this may run counter to the potentialities of plastic plumbing, which will allow much more decentralized arrangements) and the rest of the space left free. It suggests also a framing or weight-bearing system for the house which is independent of the walls, perhaps a column-and-beam arrangement, from which the walls will be hung or stretched —inner and outer walls alike. And that in turn suggests that the outer walls themselves will not stay put, but may be arranged, at different times, to take more or less of the outdoors *in,* so that the house might be conceived as an arrangement of panels and spaces on an extended frame rather than a fixed entity. The use of color, inside and outside the house, will be in translucency, in perspective, "gauzy" rather than flat. From a distance it may have somewhat the appearance of a fountain. The neighbors will hate it.

We can build our dream houses entirely of plastic—or of glass, or magnesium, or steel, or any one of a zillion other materials—but we won't. When it comes to building real houses, certain classes of materials will remain most useful for just certain classes of things. One of the great needs of the building industry is a consortium arrangement among basic producers, whereby research is not directed toward exclusive uses of materials, but the best ways of combining them for architectural purposes. As it is, in this garden of delights, the architect finds surprisingly little to be guided by.

Fuller's geodesic dome; the example here
is an aluminum auditorium in Hawaii,
seating over 2,000

He is beset on the one hand by the profusion of goods, and his obligation to choose those which best satisfy some technical requirement or human need: the ideal roof, or the best way to stay warm. He is nudged from the other side by the realization that in surrounding human living habits he is doing something to shape them, and that these habits themselves are subject to scrutiny.

Take the habit of bathing, for instance. Buckminster Fuller did, and discovered some agreement among dermatologists that Americans tend to overdo it—that constant lavings of soap and water are not particularly good for the skin. Mr. Fuller discovered a spray gun which expels a superfine mist of water (the same used in Detroit to lift the grease from automobile engines) and added a bland detergent. This contrivance, sometimes referred to as the Fuller vertical bathtub, will get you as clean as a half-hour soak, and presumably leave you healthier. Moreover, as I understand it, you don't have to remove any clothing. That the system will ever be popular is open to doubt. But Mr. Fuller has unquestionably made a point.

There are things beyond these that set the designer off balance—new conceptions of houses or housing systems to which there may appear to be an unanswerable logic. Fuller's Geodesic dome house is one: the enclosure of space in a ribbed hemisphere, covering over a maximum volume with a minimum use of material and with living spaces separately arranged inside. (Modifications of these domes are now in use for auditoriums and radar

domes, which suggests that they are something besides visionary.) Another conception for which I share Bucky Fuller's enthusiasm is that of the self-contained house. The need for connection to power, water, and sewage facilities is one of the severely limiting factors in land-development house construction. But in the autonomous house, atomic materials, ultrasonic vibrations, and a few other things which haven't been invented yet would take care of the whole works, running all equipment and processing human wastes and garbage so as to extract pure drinking water. The residue—also purified—could presumably be spread on the garden, or mailed to a distant address. The whole idea has, in fact, some distracting overtones. But also, in view of the critical, growing shortage of our water supplies, it has a rationality which cannot be ignored. Much of it is already quite possible and in limited application.

Now how does it all resolve? How does the professional architect—besieged by techniques, conceptions, materials—rediscover his lost necessities, his obligations? How is he to conceive of his work, how shall he direct his training in the future?

At the risk of incurring the disfavor of colleagues, let me remark that the fact that eighty-five per cent of houses now built go up, to all intents and purposes, without architectural supervision signalizes our remarkable failure as a group. In a season of plenty, we ourselves remain in shortage—designing fancy, individual dwellings for those most conspicuously able to pay for them, and showing the pictures to each other in glossy magazines.

The architect who designs a handsome, single house for handsome cash (and I am as guilty here as the next), however "contemporary" his design, is serving the ancient tradition of the beaux arts and is as much a kept man as the architect of the pharoahs, whose principal economic concern was the number of former enemy soldiers available to tow around blocks of limestone. I do not take it as a mortal sin (if I did, I would have upped the commission). But is it the architect's best use of himself?

He may define his mission as vaguely as to say that it is simply the design of good places for people to live. It will still follow, if he reads the clear implications of the things before discussed: the increasing mobility and concentration of our population; the increasing wealth of building techniques, means, and materials (and the fact that these materials are coming as larger, specialized units or services—panel walls rather than boards, superhighways for cart roads, heating systems for fireplace stones)—it will follow that the architect must deal in increasingly large terms with the problem of housing individuals. He must think in terms of the community or region rather than the single house; *or* in terms of the modular house, capable of industrialization, reproduction, and variation, rather than of the unique, carriage-trade house, conventionally built. To say the hard words, he must be either a regional planner or a designer for prefabrication.

These are uncomfortable thoughts for the architect. They tend to run against his habits, his aesthetic feelings, his traditional ways of envisaging himself, and even, to some extent, against the customary ethical practices of the profession. Yet whether we like it or not, we have begun to move in these directions. The evolution toward prefabrication and modularization continues as it has for centuries, and quite despite the downfall of single ventures. And the small, gallant band of regional planners—having for years done little but draw up schemes for hypothetical cities—now at last are beginning to be sought by real communities in tangible distress. The day has arrived, indeed, when a free-lance planner can support himself outside the university; I think particularly of Victor Gruen, who supplements a fine architectural sense with formidable talents as a promoter. I foresee a day, in fact, when the regular run of the architect's business will lie in the design of sub-communities where his principal materials will be houses and land, his problem the meaningful relation of them, and his parts or components will be, not lumber to make walls, but walls themselves, parts of houses, subassemblies of roofs and rooms, or whole houses, regularly produced and on the market. He will order these things in his mind as easily and habitually as today's architect thinks of two-by-fours and copper pipe.

And this, I hasten to think, is not so bad as it might sound. For one thing, it indicates an adjustment of the architect's main attention, not a diminution in the range of things which may legitimately interest him. Houses will still, in a real sense, have to be built from the ground up. But the architect will be "back in the game" where he belongs.

Few things are less comfortable than a vision half realized. Today's designer is faced with more possibilities than he knows what to do with. He is entranced with materials and enraged by their shortcomings, hidden malice, and broken promises, as well as by popular or legal conceptions of what he should or should not be allowed to do with them. But for this he needs no pity; this is at one time his grief and joy. It is, after all, what called him to the profession: a human impulse to arrange well. While, rationally, he will admit that he may never successfully design a house with the majesty of the Colossus and the lightness of a bubble; with four walls, twenty, or none; warm towel rods in the bathroom; reflective heat; and the intimacy of a sleeping bag—still, as a man in love with his work, he likes to try. These are his "kicks."

5 The Acorn House

Every architect, I suppose, looks back on his one, "best" idea: one that in any reasonable world would have brought comfort to millions, and to *him* a small measure of fame and untold folding money. He looks back on it with a mixture of love and gentle regret, as on a son who is traveling in detergents. Up to its time my own best idea was the Acorn House.

The Acorn was—I should say *is*—a demountable house: one that can be set up, taken down, trucked three or a thousand miles, and set up again as neatly as it began. It was designed as a two-bedroom affair, 24 by 35 feet. It unfolds—the bedrooms, living room and dining room—from a central core containing kitchen, bathroom, and utilities. It is factory-produced, moving as one package, by truck, to its site. Foundation work requires a total of twenty man-hours of work, three men for one day. Four men in one day can remove the house from its truck, set it up, bolt it together, install its innards, connect the utilities, and make it ready to live in. It weighs one quarter as much as a conventional frame house (six tons), is twice as strong, at least as durable, and considerably easier to heat. It was planned —on certain assumptions—to be made at a cost of $4,500 (1949 prices). Of this amount, the total cost of labor, both direct and indirect, would not exceed $350.

I use the subjunctive mood perforcedly. Today the Acorn House is neither bought nor produced. (That's where the certain assumptions come in.) The reasons will follow presently.

As to how it began: The idea of demountability, of course, is not new. The nomads of Asia have been at it for years, with houses of frame and hide—*yurts*. A tent is a demountable house of sorts. So is a trailer—though as a house it is substandard and more mobile than it needs to be—and the steady growth in the manufacture and sale of trailers is a significant factor in the housing market. Even before the second World War, there were a number of experiments with demountability or yurtdom—the most notable, perhaps, being the TVA sectional houses designed by Carroll Towne. With the coming of the war itself, experiments with this kind of house received an official impetus. The logic of the matter was simple: the government had to anticipate vast upheavals of population, both in the military service and in the relocation of civilian workers to new industrial sites in relatively undeveloped areas. And the end of the war, whenever that might come, would precipitate millions of re-relocations, and the creation of countless new families. The need of providing for all this, or enabling people to provide for themselves, was obvious, and it led to a clear choice of alternatives: either to provide "temporary" substandard housing for our migrating populations— tack and tarpaper shacks, hutments, and the like—*or* to develop a new class of dwellings, comfortable, durable, permanent, *but* relocatable. Of these alternatives, the first had the advantage of familiarity; it was what we had always done; it was quick, and, initially, cheap. But the second developed a small corps of adherents. And out of the great debate developed a series of official tests at Indian Head, Maryland.

At Indian Head, a number of building firms, mostly prefabricators, were invited to plan and erect movable houses and to submit them to a series of tests to determine the extent of their movability—their lightness, compactness, durability; their resistance to weather or damage in transit; their rebuildability; and the like.

I went to Indian Head as an observer, several times on my own and later for the Defense Housing Office, to see the results of these tests. They were not impressive.

Most of the houses were, in effect, conventionally designed and built, except for being joined, in sections, by double-headed nails. Pull the nails out, move the sections, and drive them in again. There was an elementary sense to it—but also a dire waste of materials, equipment, and labor. And after being transplanted even once, the houses began to curl around the edges. I still remember the sight of one model as it heaved slowly across a field on a twelve-wheel truck—its roof hanging and flapping over the side like the wings of a torpid vulture.

Even if the Indian Head experiments had been uniformly successful, I think we still would have had the kind of war housing we eventually got, and all remember: acres and acres of rickety, bare board carpentry. One irony of the matter is that to most people *this* is the kind of building that the word "prefabrication" suggests. Another, more serious, is that, although it was cheap at the start, it was wastefully done, uncomfortable, expensive to maintain, and that by now the bulk of it represents a dead loss. Written off as war expenditure—millions of dollars.

The idea of an adequate demountable house, or any house so fabricated as to require a minimum of site labor, hung in my mind until the end of the war (I did my own brief stretch on the staff of the Naval Radar Training School). At war's end I was further stimulated to read about vast available amounts of surplus material. Aluminum, for instance—the airplane makers had lots and lots of aluminum and nowhere to put it. I began trying to bring the idea together with the realities.

In the last chapter I mentioned the advantages of "stressed-skin" walls—sandwich constructions—of which the inner and outer sheathing is structurally bonded to the framing or separating members. In point of their lightness and strength, such walls were obviously material to my purpose. I began casting about for a likely one.

Now if you take a strip of paper, say one by twelve inches, this would not seem much to build with:

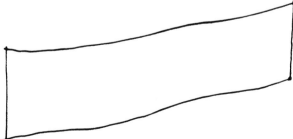

but if you turn it edgewise and crease or corrugate it, you increase its compressive strength tremendously.

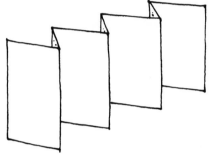

If you combine it with other strips of paper, in any of a number of ways—a honeycomb pattern, for instance—you get something which will bear an even weight of one hundred pounds per square inch.

Thus:

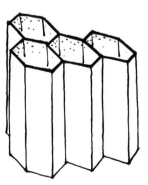

This sort of paper construction was used as early as 1871, in corrugated paper cartons. It has been further developed and modified by a number of people—for instance, the Forest Products Laboratory has done a considerable amount of development work on it over the past fifteen years. If, as they showed, you impregnate the paper honeycomb with plastic and glue it rigidly to a sheathing material, you get what is known as a stressed-skin construction, which has strength and insulative ability out of all proportion to its weight and at a theoretically very low cost.

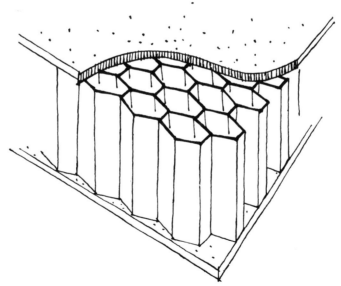

What to use as a sheathing material? Well, plywood was an obvious possibility, or any of the composition wood materials, or sheet steel, or, indeed, aluminum. Which is where the aircraft companies came in—or I thought they would.

Here, at any rate, was an estimable means of enclosing space—but how much space, of what shape, and how divided up? Here there was a handy necessity: if the house were to be portable by truck, no section of it should exceed a width of eight feet. The question then was, what parts of a house might be designed, sawed, folded, or otherwise compressed into eight-foot widths, and what might not? It seemed reasonable that one such section, 8 by 24 feet, should comprise the utilities "core" of the house: the kitchen and bathroom, plumbing, heating apparatus, and the like. The reasons for this were several. For one thing, eight feet is a good width for a kitchen. For a second, the centralizing of pipes, pumps, tanks, and so on facilitates "hooking up," keeps connections short, and—most important—lends itself to preassembly of the core in the factory, rather than on the site by hitches and starts. (The cost of utilities in a conventional house is almost one quarter of the total. The stringing of pipes to widely separated areas, and the innumerable, individual, tasteful ways of hitching them up, have raised plumbing from a craft to a fine, expensive art. It is in the design and acceptance of prefabricated utilities systems—to digress for a moment—that the next major "breakthrough" of the industry might come. That, and the discovery of an all-purpose, all-soils, precast foundation system.) For a third reason, to anticipate a point, it's hard to fold a bathtub.

As to the arrangement of room space *around* the utilities core—by conceiving of it as, in fact, empty, symmetrical space, and planning to divide it not by attached interior walls but by room-separator cabinets—it proved possible to enclose all of it by floor and wall panels which were hinged to, and swung out from, the core section.

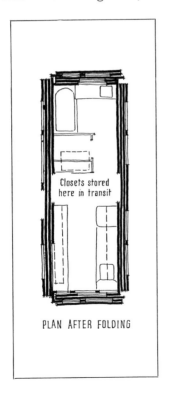

Closets stored
here in transit

PLAN AFTER FOLDING

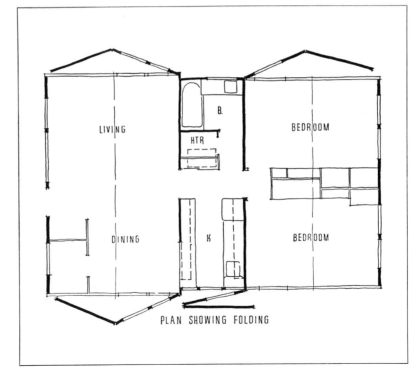

LIVING

B.

HTR

BEDROOM

DINING

K

BEDROOM

PLAN SHOWING FOLDING

(I should make special note that in all beyond the elementary stages of the design, I was working with architects Huson Jackson and John Callender in Cambridge, Massachusetts, under the office name of Planning and Building Associates. Both of them spent long hours wrestling with details of the Acorn design, to no profit but that of their souls. After our triumvirate dissolved, both retained interests in the Acorn House—like an excursion ticket to the kingdom of Prester John.)

All along, there was the problem of a foundation system for the house. Structurally it required none—or only enough to ride on. Was there such a thing as a demountable foundation? A series of jacks, for instance, which would adjust to keep the house trimmed level in spite of frost heavings in the earth? Or, if we used a solid foundation, could we confine it to the area beneath the utilities core and cantilever out the two wings of the house? We were much engaged with both possibilities, but we abandoned both when they began to look tricky, and settled with the following: eight holes dug down to below frost line, a couple of feet wide and three to five feet deep; prefabricated concrete posts suspended in these holes; and footings poured around them with steel beams bolted level across the top. (The pouring of footings could go on with the house already bolted in place, temporarily supported on blocks.)

Total cost of foundation work, including all material and labor, but excluding the cost of the steel beams which, like the house, were demountable, would be about seventy

The Acorn foundation

dollars. This, as compared with usual foundation costs, in New England anyway, of about six hundred dollars.

In all of the foregoing, but particularly when it came to arranging the innards of the house, we found ourselves, as architects, carried into small considerations which architects are happiest to ignore: the design of hinges, the price of medicine cabinets, and the altitude of potty seats. We had to reconcile a strict economy of space and cost with the imponderables of grace and amenity. How much of the furnishings, storage space, and appliances should be "built in," how much should be left for the owner to arrange? How many of these things could be procured from regular sources—a small factory, say, in Terre Haute—and how many should we design new, for ourselves? (In theory the new design of a house, particularly a house for mass production, may extend to minutiae: the details of blower motors, the rehousing of hot-water equipment, or even, to take an extreme example, the wrapping of electric wires. In practice, of course, every design rests on certain assumptions, or rather decisions—as, for instance, that a bathtub is not foldable—about which there is not truth or falsity but a comforting sense of usage. Every architect must adapt his sense of efficiency and elegance to what is commercially available and in quantity.) To give an example: For the kitchen we found a regular, "famous-name" clothes- and dishwasher which was sufficiently compact to meet our peculiar space requirements, but no stove, and no regular refrigerator. So we designed a stove in two parts: separate burners set into the counter tops, and a separate, waist-high oven. We designed a drawer-type refrigerator which, though hardly in regular production, was happily worked out for us by a young and enthusiastic company. They would give us a pilot model. They did. (It didn't work so well, either, as it turned out.) In the last few years, two of these items, the counter-top stove and the separate oven, have been worked over, slicked up, and popularly accepted. At that time, they hadn't. And while the credit for their success is distinctly not ours, it all goes to prove something or other.

By early 1946, our plans for the house were complete enough so that we could look for a means of getting it into production. And here began a whole new education. We went to the aircraft companies. They, remember, had that tremendous, burdensome surplus of aluminum as well as experience in stressed-skin fabrication. Since they weren't making many planes any more, we asked, would they be interested in making houses? Why, yes, they decided, sure they would. Maybe even a kind of queerish-looking house like this. *If* the government would put up a few million dollars to get the thing started for them. After all, that's how they made planes—cost-plus and all that.

We went to the government and received a generous share of interest and some hopes of loan assistance. But nothing so practical and immediate as to jolt the airplane people into action.

We went to the aluminum companies themselves. Like the aircraft companies, they were feeling the pinch, but they weren't just sure they wanted to manufacture whole houses. I remember the research director of one of the largest companies, who was pinning his bright future hopes for housing on the making of doorknobs.

(Subsequently, of course, the aluminum folk set to work and developed a host of new products. The wisdom of the planemakers in sitting on their hands was demonstrated by the resurgence of the national peril and a host of new subsidies. And the Lustron Housing Corporation put the arm on the Reconstruction Finance Corporation for over thirty million dollars. It's all a matter of timing.)

I continued my pilgrimages—to the military services, labor unions, private financiers—but the edge of our optimism had begun to dull when John Bemis wandered onto the scene. He became, and remains, the moving force behind the Acorn House. John is a tall, taciturn New Englander, the son of Albert Farwell Bemis, mentioned earlier as a successful pioneer builder, and he is an experienced engineer himself. Yet by inclination he is nothing so much as a peripatetic latter-day Yankee inventor, and the Acorn House appealed mightily to his tinkering instinct.

John settled in a corner for half a year or more, working over detail drawings, making phone calls to such research institutes as the Forest Products Laboratory, testing samples of materials, and humming under his breath. At the end of that time, he stood up quietly and announced that if no one else was going to build the house, then, by gollies, *he* would.

This was more of an undertaking than it sounds. To build a single, conventional house is no great trick. To build a factory-produced house, you need a factory. For even a trial-model Acorn, built slowly and mostly by hand, the capital investment was disproportionate. This is the central problem, as noted, of all beginning ventures in prefabrication.

But John undertook to raise the cash, and we incorporated ourselves. (We were never quite content with the name Acorn, but it sat better than the alternatives suggested: "Environmental Modifiers, Inc.," "Resin-dences," and "Folding Homes." Architects have many witty friends.) He occupied a shed in the Boston and Maine freight yards in Charlestown, built a giant press for fabricating the wall and floor panels (not then or now commercially available), and assembled the necessary minimum of machinery. From there he later moved to an abandoned recreation hall at the military airfield in Bedford.

By early summer of 1947, all the panels had been fabricated, glued, and pressed. (We started from scratch, with bulk paper, using plywood for sheathing; after the aluminum companies had snubbed us, we snubbed *them*.) Along the way, we had aroused a measure of public interest, and *Life* magazine had proposed to cover the erection. What we needed now was a place to erect.

To understand our difficulties in this regard, you need only reflect on the matter of building codes, mentioned earlier, and on how vastly different the Acorn was from what people were used to. In appearance, to be sure, it was rather unobtrusive and demure, but with respect to structure, particularly in methods of plumbing, framing, and foundation, it was probably in violation, on fifteen or more counts, of the building codes of every town in New England. That it was superior on all counts to most houses constructed by code was, as we would discover, nothing to the point.

We had made a deliberate choice—and with some foreknowledge of the consequences —to design an unconventional house. Simply because conventional methods and materials could never offer the same results, strengths, or economics. As we worked on, and as we were better convinced of the sense of what we did—it was apparent to *us* that there was nothing "theatrical" about it—we tended to assume that the sense of it would be immediately apparent to others. This is the kind of assumption that an architect can be guilty of—but a politician, never.

———————————————————————

Our appearances before the building inspectors of several towns, and from them to the boards of appeal, began to follow a pattern. From what provisions of the code, they would ask, did we want exception? Well—we would choose somewhat at random—for instance, this provision here, that studs shall be two by four or better, set at intervals of not more than sixteen inches on center. How come—did we want to space them wider? Well, no, we would say, as a matter of fact—well, it's just that the Acorn doesn't *have* studs. Their jaws unhinged.

At a point they would call for designs and drawings, and peer down at them with the same uneasy wonder as a man whose wife has taken up poker. Lookit here, they would say —how it perches up off the ground—a house like that would get cold! We would demonstrate that the thermal-conductivity value of the paper-core panels was .196 British thermal units per square foot, per hour, per degree Fahrenheit, which is to say, very good indeed. But a house with paper walls—my God, did you say paper? What happens in wet weather? We would explain that the paper, besides being *inside* the wall, was plastic impregnated, and had exceptional resistance to rot or deterioration—90 per cent wet strength, that is. But it's flimsy, isn't it? We would produce data on the panels: sheer strength of the core about seventy pounds per square inch, compressive strength of the panels proper about seven thousand pounds per square foot. But a house that comes on a truck, and unfolds, and has *hinges* in it! More data, on over-all strength. But look at that foundation, it wouldn't support a meringue.

Because of the Acorn's light weight, we would explain, it wasn't a matter of holding it up as much as bolting it down. But that's what we meant—flimsy. The data again. But anyway, someone would conclude triumphantly, the way it perches up off the ground—a house like that would get cold.

There is an extent to which the questions you are asked are susceptible to technical answers and an extent beyond that in which you must bear a burden of proof against sentiment and preconception. To take, for example, the fact that the Acorn House is lightweight: To me its lightness and tautness and resiliency are joyful, like that of a boat. But to generations of good citizens, lightness is equated with weakness, destructibility. (To their children, this will not seem so obvious.) To take another example: the looks of the Acorn, in sitting above the ground. To many this is reminiscent of Army-hutment construction, and all the drafty, uncomfortable things that went with *that*.

I recall one appearance before a three-man board of appeal in the town of Belmont, where I lived at the time. After a considerable preliminary discussion, one member of the board—to whom I shall always be obliged—ventured this opinion: that he didn't particularly like the "modern" looks of the house, he wouldn't want to live in it himself; in short, it wasn't at all his cup of tea. But the engineering data, so far as he could see, were convincing. Further, the architect Carl Koch had built a number of acceptable houses here in Belmont, was a Belmont resident himself, and, so far as he knew, had never struck his mother with a closed fist. So all in all, as he understood his responsibilities, if Koch was willing to risk his reputation, he himself had no choice but to approve our request.

The second member spoke up. "I," he said, "was elected to stop the building of cracker boxes in the town of Belmont."

The first member begged his pardon—but he was exceeding his authority. If the house was structurally sound, safe, and healthful, he couldn't deny permission just because he didn't like its looks.

"I," said the second member, "was elected to stop cracker boxes in the town of Belmont."

Dammit, said the first member, this is a matter of individual rights. There is a buyer in Belmont who wants this house to live in. As long as he lives lawfully, he has a right to live any way he likes. Take his own house, said the first member—if he wanted to paint it in alternate red and green stripes, he figured that was his privilege, and let anyone try to stop him.

The second member ignored him, and gazed fixedly at the third. "Are you," he asked, "in favor of cracker boxes in the town of Belmont?"

That ended it.

The first Acorn House went up in the town of Concord. Concord, besides Yankee intransigence, has to this day retained a strict Yankee sense of what is a man's own private business. This is the town that stood up and was counted at the start of the American Revolution, and, a few generations later, gave roof to Emerson, Hawthorne, and the rest of that restless, transcendental crew. By Concord we were granted a two-year permit to build on the land of Gordon Hutchins. "And if," as one of the board members put it, "the house doesn't work out just right for humans—well, I know Gordon likes to keep pigs and chickens, and I expect he can still find a use for it."

The Acorn moved into Concord by truck in November, 1948, escorted by a cadre of *Life* reporters; Ezra Stoller, the noted architectural photographer; assorted small children; and two bemused patrolmen. It was set up handily and furnished, with short delays, while Stoller took pictures and the *Life* men reported, all without incident—until one of the *Life* men appeared at John Bemis's elbow.

"I've got an idea for tomorrow," said the *Life* man. "We'll take the roof off again."

The idea, it turned out, besides taking the roof off, was to hire a helicopter, put Ezra Stoller in it, and take pictures of the house *straight down.* It was all a little outside John's experience, but here he was, face to face with *Life,* and he realized he should think big. Anyway, it was easier than turning the house on its side.

The next day was cool and blustery. The roof was folded back, struck by a gust of wind, and wrestled with like a sail in a squall. The crew waited for signs of either the whirly bird or rain. Toward the end of the morning, a call arrived from the helicopter people in Connecticut. The craft rented for the occasion had become involved with a young fir tree and now reposed in a creek bottom. They were sending another.

By midafternoon the second arrived, and landed at the Bedford Airport. Ezra Stoller, whose enthusiasm for the project had waned with each advancing hour, drove over and buckled himself into it. (As a photographer of houses and furnished interiors, Ezra seldom dealt with anything more mobile than a Dalmatian.) As the helicopter clattered over the horizon, arrived, and hovered, he hung gamely over the side, alternately peering into his view finder and signaling the pilot, tight-lipped, to hold the damn thing still.

Down below, things were almost as lively. The walls of the Acorn vibrated in sympathy with the rotors. The tremendous downdraft of air hit the floor of the house, and bounced. A small rug sailed up over the side and southward. A table jittered magically across the floor and wedged itself into a corner. The drapery surrounding each window streamed raggedly up like the gallant banners on Marye's Heights. Ezra, up above, worked his camera many times. I have never seen the results of his day's work, but many fine pictures were taken, from below, of Ezra.

The *Life* article came out in January of 1949. "Handsome, cheap and sensible," *Life* called the house, and added candidly, "It may never be available." The article went on to speak of the matter of building codes—some cities requiring six-inch foundation walls, others

twelve, while the Acorn had none, of either. Ordinances requiring cellars, or prohibiting flat roofs, or requiring that all plumbing joints be made within the city limits, and so on. And beyond that, the reluctance of loan bankers to finance prefabrication ventures. (This reluctance has somewhat abated since that time; in other respects the article still stands.)

Architectural Record paid the house a visit a while later, and was favorably impressed:

"Space within the Acorn House may seem small, but we discovered that there is no cramped feeling. Perhaps this is because so much furniture and equipment, ordinarily portable, is built in. . . . We had expected some sense of impermanence, but, pleasantly, found little such evidence; floors were no more springy than in the average house; windows and other details were small in scale, and enhanced the feeling of spaciousness."

It was good publicity, and aroused a considerable response. We received several thousands of letters from legitimate, interested buyers, as well as many offers of land to put up more samples on. And a few messages, under important-seeming letterheads, saying, "If you can deliver four thousand units in the next three months, maybe we can talk business." (We couldn't exactly, and neither, as it worked out, could they.)

Over the period of the next year or so, we followed down as many leads as we could. But we were beset by the same problem we had begun with—the chicken and the egg: without a demonstrated product, no capital, no plant. Without capital and plant, no product to demonstrate. In order to quote a sensible price to prospective buyers, we would have to produce in volume, with workers and machinery—and, initially, from a deficit basis. That was the one element we had already in hand: the deficit. We did have prepared, by a firm of consulting engineers, a painstaking estimate of manufacturing costs, of which I quoted some results at the beginning of this chapter. But the certain assumptions with which it began included $330,000 worth of machinery and a productive rate of eight houses per day—than which a trip to the moon was easier.

By now it was obvious, even to me, that the Acorn was a slow grower. I joined forces with two young architects, Leon Lipshutz and Fritz Day, and we began to accumulate a respectable practice—individual houses, libraries, banks, and the like—which continues to the present, alongside the ventures discussed later.

In 1951, things looked up a little. The government—the Housing and Home Finance Agency—became interested again in the possibility of relocatable houses for use in places like atomic-energy installations and military outposts. The characteristics of the Acorn—its foundation system, insulative properties, and the fact that it could travel all in one lump—recommended it for this sort of thing. We were invited to participate in a series of tests similar to the old Indian Head experiments, accepted, built another Acorn demonstration house, and entered it with the houses of seven other firms. The tests were encouraging. We were then asked to submit a bid for the construction of fifty houses for the Navy, in Virginia.

Three interior views of the Acorn House

Photographs by Ezra Stoller

This matter came within the purview of the local Public Housing Authority, which, by and large, was less friendly than the HHFA. Discussion went on for a number of months. We were down to the finest and we hoped final points when, in 1952, administrations changed. Mr. Eisenhower came into office, and along with him Mr. Wilson—and one of Mr. Wilson's first economy measures was to cut out all this kind of tomfoolishness. We sold the demonstration model to a man in Dover, Massachusetts.

We thought of, and tried for a time, selling scaled-down Acorns for summer cottages, hunting lodges, and the like. One of the design problems here was that, for a summer cottage, the Acorn was a whole lot better than it had to be. It was something we should have thought of sooner. We made about half a dozen.

Taken all in all, it's accurate, though easy, to say that the Acorn was designed for a time not yet arrived. We knew something of that before we began. We built it—at least two of it—in a period decidedly inimical to prefabrication (of 280 companies entering this field in 1946, 60 were still alive and staggering by 1949), in the presence of restrictive codes, official and financial disinterest, and before conventional housing had begun, as it now has, to price itself out of the market. I can still be pleased that we did not design it differently.

The Acorn House is still in Concord—out Monument Street on Punkatasset Hill, though you probably wouldn't notice it, driving by—still trim, tight, and warm. Acorn

Houses, Inc., is still alive, though John Bemis's press is turning out panels for the Techbuilt house. John himself bides his time; it's a Yankee habit.

Any day now we expect to hear that the government has hit upon the idea of demountable housing, and is considering a series of tests to evaluate it. Might invite a number of firms to design and enter houses. In fact, I know where they might do it all. Place called Indian Head. . . .

6 Lustron

When, finally, the Acorn House was ready for a grateful public—at this writing, eight years later, it's still ready—I was fortunate enough to get an assignment for Carl Koch and Associates as architectural consultants to the Lustron Corporation.

The Lustron venture itself will be long remembered. Nothing on its scale had been tried before—or has since. It represented an investment of thirty-five million dollars, most of it in loans from the government's Reconstruction Finance Corporation. It undertook to prefabricate houses at something like ten times the previous combined rate of the rest of the industry.

The houses themselves were of steel, frame and walls alike, with a finish coat of porcelain enamel. This is a material often used, in shinier form, it must be noted, for store fronts, gas stations, and, indeed, kitchen sinks. It is variable in texture and gloss, neat, strong, easy to maintain, and infinitely durable.

Plans eventually called for the production of forty thousand Lustron houses a year, one every seven working minutes. Three thousand, as it turned out, actually *did* get made and erected. The final dead loss was upwards of thirty million dollars, almost all of it in public money.

Our own connection with the enterprise was brief. But when I leaf back through the

records—plans, brochures, contracts, the transcript of Congressional autopsies—I admit to a confusion of feelings between the way we regarded it then, even from the outside, and the way it turned out to be. Seldom has there occurred a like mixture of idealism, greed, efficiency, stupidity, potential social good, and political evil. Seldom, surely, has a good idea come so close to realization, and been so decisively slugged.

Lustron was established in a square mile of factory, previously an airplane plant, outside of Columbus, Ohio. I remember when Fritz and Leon, my two associates, and I made our first tour through the premises on a motor wagon, gazing at acres of machinery. Even by American mass-production standards, it was an impressive layout. With everything going at once, it used as much electric current as Columbus proper. The houses themselves started at one end as rolls of steel, bar stock, or other elementary metal shapes, and from there were moved by conveyor; sliced, punched, stamped, or otherwise bashed; welded, riveted, bolted, as the case might be; or sprayed and baked—finally issuing at the other end as packages of three thousand component parts, loaded on special trailers and ready to go.

That, at any rate, is how it was supposed to be. As to how it went in practice—the story of the bathtub machine, I think, is indicative. The bathtub machine, a giant press, sat square in the middle of the works. It was the largest contrivance I had ever seen, reaching about three stories above ground and two below. What it did, as you might suppose, was to take a single, flat piece of metal, make preliminary whirring sounds, and tnen wallop it decisively into a complete bathtub shape. Its music was impressive.

This press had been procured at enormous expense to turn out individual tubs very cheaply, something like $15 as opposed to a wholesale lot price of around $45. But it soon developed that in order to operate efficiently, and amortize its original cost, it would have to turn out 120,000 tubs a year—40,000 of them for Lustron houses, the rest to be sold on the open market. However, the tubs it made to fit the Lustron house were five feet, one and a half inches long. And almost nowhere in the world can you sell a bathtub of that size. Five feet even, yes. Five feet, one and a half inches, no. At that point, as at several others, Lustron experienced a change of production managers.

The purpose for which we ourselves had been hired—Fritz, Leon and I, with a lot of help from expert associates at M.I.T. in metal, color, administration, and a couple of other subjects—was the redesign of the original Lustron house. (The original had been in process for quite a while. At the time of our arrival, the first experimental models were coming off the line, and being hitched together to see how they fit.) Our new design, if things went well, was scheduled to appear in 1950. Concerning it, our instructions from Lustron were simple enough, at least outwardly. To plan a house that was good-looking, nicely proportioned—in a word, beautiful. Then they, engineers and production men, would take the plans, and figure how to make it all out of metal.

The instructions were intended in good faith to put as few limitations as possible on our presumed creativity. Yet, beset by good faith, we could only fumble for ways to explain that this just wasn't the way you did it; that you don't get a good house by designing the common man's castle in a vacuum; that planning starts from necessities; that, to return to a previous point, the design of a house is in no way separable from the ways in which it is to be made, or even distributed. These requirements may lead an architect to a study of the hand-and-arm movements of workmen, the axle loading of trucks or the political organization of ancient Rome. Each with a demonstrable application to his business. And if architecture in these terms remains an art, it is an art with its own peculiar dimensions.

So that what we had to do, conscientiously, was to educate ourselves in the workings of the Lustron machinery: rolls, punch presses, frit grinders, enameling ovens. We must follow the course of any individual piece of metal, from the time it entered the factory doors to the time it was unloaded on site a thousand miles away, and know what had to be ready at the site, waiting for it.

Why we should want to know all these things was a mystery to Lustron. But if we wanted to work harder than we had to, they supposed it was all right.

We began by visiting the spots where the pilot models were being erected. (They were supposed to go up on site in 150 man-hours or less. And after the first few, they did. But these originals took closer to 1,000 man-hours, and gave everyone the feeling of being involved in a bad dream.) Starting at that end, we worked our way back, trying to understand each process we came to. Though we had been acquainted with industrialized houses for some time, it had never been on this scale. I remember thinking how far the times had led me away from my first formal schooling in architecture, which had commenced with the drawing of columns in the Ionic mode. But in time we gained some sense, if not understanding, of the machine process, not as vast and inhuman, but sensible, occasionally oversimple, subject to its own freakish humors, and managed by people not so much smarter, after all, than we.

There were many splendid things about the house, we discovered—a new and remarkably effective heating system was one (radiant, from the ceiling). Another was the enameling process itself—the baking of the finish onto the steel at a lower temperature than previously possible, with lighter-gauge steel and in only two cookings. So far as wearing qualities were concerned, of course, the surface material was marvelous.

At the same time we discovered some puzzling things. For one thing, the house had never been architected in a real sense. It had started with some sketches drawn by a Chicago architect, which proved to be remarkably good and workable, considering that neither he nor Lustron at the start knew just how different components would be produced. But there had been little opportunity for follow-through and many things had been worked out as they went along. Another thing—surprising in an undertaking of this size—was that little serious thought had yet been given to the pre-assembly of parts in the factory. They arrived on the building site in a package, sure enough, but all three thousand pieces as separate as lumber.

Lustron had on hand a regular staff of "stylists," most of them veterans of the automobile industry. They had served as the entrepreneurs of the first design and had been to some pains to keep it from looking "prefabricated." In it they had included a certain number of sure-fire "selling points": a bay-window section, an ornamental pier or pillar or pilaster at the corner of the house, a recessed bookcase in the living-room wall, a wonderfully nubile window frame, and the like. When we began to question some of these features, and the number and overdesign of some parts, their attitude stiffened somewhat. (Multiplicity of parts, after all, is of no great concern in the making of cars, and assembly no problem for the dealers.) The stylists were uniformly cooperative and courteous, but I think it is fair to say we liked them better than they liked us.

As weeks went by we began to edge our way cautiously toward a new design, one that would require fewer and simpler parts, make better use of them, and even, perhaps, permit the building of not one but several different houses—all without basic changes in Lustron's equipment or sequence of operations. (We were interested, for instance, in the possibility of a three-bedroom house, a statistical necessity for the postwar family, but curiously rare at the time.)

Along the way we bumped up against a fair share of technical problems. One of them was—or rather, had been—that the furnaces which did the actual baking of the enamel coating onto the steel were not designed efficiently to accommodate panels larger than two feet square. This had resulted in two drawbacks. In order to prevent leaks, each individual panel had to be set off from its neighbors by a polyvinyl-chloride plastic gasket—which is hard enough even to pronounce. A single wall used up yards and yards of gasket and hours of hand labor on the building site. And it took ludicrous, long research to find a way of insuring a tight seal at the point where the four corners came together.

Besides that: Although steel itself is a structural material with great strength in both tension and compression, with this system of small panels its strength was wasted. Framing members were erected, much like the studding in a regular house, and then the panels were hung to them, after the fashion of shingles. The house weighed about twelve tons, altogether, half of it holding the other half up. And this overuse of material, while it might have helped make the first house attractive to the skeptical, was bound to hoist its price.

By the time we arrived on the scene, happily a way had been found to accommodate larger panel sizes in the ovens. So, taking all these things together, one of our first recommendations was that panel size be increased to two by eight feet—floor to ceiling—and that panels be rolled out and cut to lengths in a continuous-line process, rather than cut and punched intermittently. This in itself would do more work, more quickly, with much less expensive equipment. We designed, or rather adapted, a system of vertical creasing, or ribbing, of these two-by-eight panels, which increased their strength as load-bearing members and did away with all the heavy studwork. Joints between panels, because of the ribbing, were concealed, and there was no longer any need for gaskets.

The recommendation was fairly obvious. And an obvious example, too, of why our original marching orders—just to design a handsome house and not worry about production matters—could have led us far astray. This aspect of the new design was accepted fairly handily, despite opposition from some of the stylists who weren't sure it was handsome enough, and from some production men who—such is the force of even new habit—were already used to doing it the other way. It was accepted because, though it would require a great deal of new and expensive equipment, retooling, and layout, it would pay for itself in a few months from savings in labor and material, not to mention long-term customer satisfaction in freedom from maintenance and leakage.

Filled with confidence, we went after the roof design. The roof was of panels, like the walls. Roof panels had to fit tightly without gaskets, and the problem of making them weatherproof was even more serious. (During all the time we were in service, there was one engineer who sat quietly in a corner with this problem, trying out different shapes and sizes, drawing pictures, and muttering to himself.) We were mainly disturbed, however, that the roof panels were embossed to simulate Spanish tile. We thought it looked awful.

But when we arrived with our packet of roof suggestions, we were told that, in the first place, the shape of the panels had been carefully calculated as the most economical use of steel plate in spanning the necessary distance. And that, in the second place, Lustron had several millions of dollars tied up in the machines that produced them, so the roof wasn't going to be changed, and that was that.

Ever inventive, we resolved this problem by deciding the roof didn't look so bad after all. In our two major reports to Lustron, some of the more successful aspects were these:

1. The original Lustron model used four different sizes of window in a fixed arrangement. We reduced them to one—but so designed as to be triple-hung and completely interchangeable with solid wall panels of the same size, so that we could

make any combination with these few panels. Putting two such sections side by side would permit not twelve but thirty-six variations. Three, side by side, would offer two hundred and sixteen. Not all of them would be useful, needless to say, but the law of combinations is one of the pleasant mathematical secrets of modular planning.

2. Since the enameled walls of the Lustron house were permanent, in and out (the enamel would chip away in places when the house was put together, but was easily patched), it followed that wall color was permanent too. This could be a little hard on a housewife who, having lived with green surroundings for several years, might suddenly decide she liked brown better, or yellow, or white. If green was what she had selected, green was what she had. So what we recommended was that inside wall color be made as unobtrusive as possible, neutral—shades of gray, in fact. Then the color motif of the house could be established by the housewife herself, by the generous use of color in rugs, fabrics, furniture, drapes, and the like—things that *could* be changed.

3. The original Lustron house was fixed, as to size and interior plan. We discovered, working with a basic size of 29 by 37 feet, and an expanded size of 29 by 45 feet, that Lustron could offer four different interior plans in each, including several for three bedrooms. Any of these plans, moreover, could be "flipped," that is to say,

built as a mirror image of itself. And all plans, together, would use the same component parts, with virtually no exception.

4. The number of separate components which would arrive by truck, to be assembled on site by individual builders, we reduced from three thousand to thirty-seven by providing for the assembly of window sections, storage walls, plumbing walls, and so forth in the plant itself. Lustron, indeed, was already on the trail of this simplification.

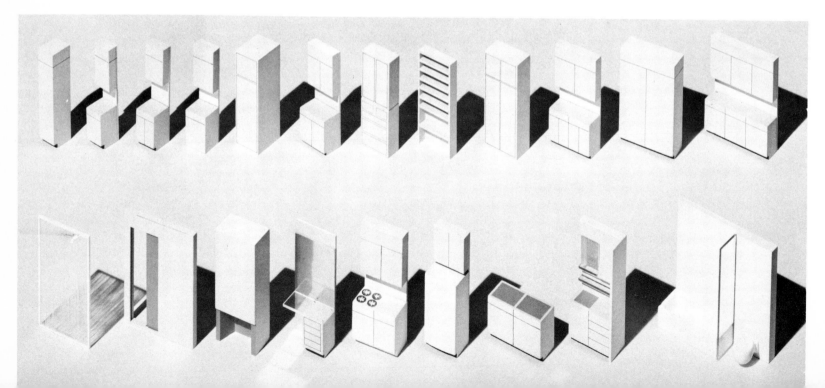

This was not just a paper saving, since the matter of putting small pieces together to form bigger ones is better done by skilled labor, under controlled conditions, than by local builders' crews, slithering around in rainy weather, and trampling braces into the long grass.

We tried, without notable success, to draw Lustron's attention to land and community problems. Since, as often as not, the house would be built in developments of fifty or more, it followed that these developments should be so planned as to allow for some variety in the way different houses were placed on the land, landscaped, fenced or enclosed by trees; and in the addition of carports, garages or breezeways at different angles. But the Lustron management tended to feel they had enough headaches there at home without worrying about what happened upcountry. Therefore, we had to design a house which would fit on a fifty-foot lot and could be sited in different directions to take advantage of the sun, or different ways of access, and hope piously that the lots would be bigger than fifty feet wide.

Since the house would be built many times over, we had to look with a cold eye on some of the decorative motifs on the first model. They looked fine—once. Twenty times over, they began to get tiresome. So we wrenched loose the ornamental pillar at the corner of the porch, and the recessed bookcase and the bay window. The breast-shaped window frame fell, so to speak, of its own weight; it had turned out to leak.

On these counts, as on several others, we were engaged in a polite, running skirmish with the stylists. After we submitted our first report, neatly done up in a cellophane cover, forty pages deep and illustrated, the stylists came through with one of their own, wider, deeper, and prettier. In our second report we held the line on page size, but we did snap up the cover photograph, bear down on layout, and include a number of pictures more decorative than essential. The stylists' second report came complete in color with a cellophane overlay, was the size of a small desk in area, and required a two-man detail to turn the pages. I don't know where we could have gone from there, but the first stage of our work was done.

We had shown it possible to reduce the number of component parts of the house, both in the absolute and with respect to the "package" that builders would receive. In general we had reduced the complexity of parts, and as a result the size and complexity of machinery that would fabricate them. We had substantially increased their interchangeability. We had reduced the weight of material in the house from about twelve to about nine tons, without any loss of strength, and vastly simplified the problem of assembly in the field. We had much increased the variety of plans from which the individual buyer might choose, and reduced, it was clear, the price he should have to pay for it.

The house was scheduled for production in 1950, and we settled down to the business of making detailed plans.

Photographs by Robert D. Harvey Studio

**Exterior of proposed
1950 Lustron Model House
and (*right*) living room**

Above, bedroom of
1950 Lustron Model House
and (*below*) dining area

Photographs by Robert D. Harvey Studio

I well remember the vigor and eloquence with which, speaking on behalf of Lustron, I addressed the 1949 Ann Arbor Conference on Developments in the Construction Industry. The date was April first.

"Lustron has tooled up its plant. Its product has attained unheard of acceptability. Its dealers are poised for large volume, and reasonable profit on a quick turn-over. Lustron today is moving through the last phases of its predevelopment period. Tomorrow, those men who put their faith in an idea will have their judgment confirmed, and the American consumer will have a new standard for living."

Subsequently the Lustron Corporation hoisted sail, and moved slowly and majestically into receivership.

7 Conantum

Only the recording angels have the whole cumbersome history of Lustron, and even for them it must raise some fine points of interpretation. But it contains a few familiar lessons for the earthbound:

There's no question, for one thing, that Lustron felt the curses of bigness: group thinking, a tendency to batter down small problems with large money, and a kind of institutional absent-mindedness. The preoccupation of Lustron with its own internal doings showed itself, by example, in the conviction that if the house were good, and inexpensive—as it was—that matters of distribution, dealership, and sales would somehow take care of themselves. As if it were enough, in effect, to bring the house to the factory door, where the avid public could snatch it up.

It seems clear, at the same time, that the basic "idea" of Lustron was sound, and most of its problems well solved. To a most considerable extent Lustron was the victim not of mismanagement but of circumstances. (The venture was delayed for a year at the beginning, in a contest with the makers of the celebrated Tucker automobile for possession of a critical manufacturing plant. And this year's delay meant in turn that the first Lustron houses hit the market spang in the middle of the first-quarter-of-1949 recession.) All in all, it would appear that a little more money, ventured at the critical time, might have saved what was lost. But this, of course, is the gambler's choice, and the government is not, nor should be, an easy gambler. From the point of view of the RFC, a lot had already been spent. And that agency was under considerable pressure from builders, suppliers, and manufacturers who saw in Lustron a threat to their own settled way of doing business. Though a loan is a far cry from outright subsidy, the question of government subsidy was—and is—in question.

(On that point, there is as much good opinion on one side as the other. The advocates of subsidy point out that few enterprises as massive as prefabrication have got started without it. For the railroads, in their early days, there was the business of land grants. For the makers of automobiles, for trucking and allied industries, there is a constant indirect subsidy in the building and maintenance of highways. And it can surely be argued that economical housing offers as many social benefits as those, and is no more disruptive of established interests. On the other hand, as opponents of subsidy point out, it now appears that prefabrication will come along anyway, in its own time, in its own way; that it has indeed been capable of starting small, and though, as a free enterprise, it comes slowly, the principle may be worth the delay.)

After Lustron, and an interval of more routine practice, Fritz, Leon, and I were invited to participate in a smaller, more thoroughgoing, and a good deal more satisfying venture: to act as designers of the Conantum community.

Between the two—Lustron and Conantum—there is one dour resemblance. Both went broke. But beyond that point, while the first stayed broke, the second went on to a successful completion. Conantum's troubles resulted, not from gross miscalculation but an effort to calculate too closely—to do too much, too neatly, on too small a bankroll. A consideration of what the "lost" money finally went to buy—in both the present, financial, net worth of the community and its intangible uncountable worth as a place to live—suggests that it might have been cheap at twice the price. There are few places like it.

Though the Conantum venture was in some respects unique, the ideas behind it were not new; it's difficult to find a starting point. The prime mover of the undertaking, however, was Professor Rupert Maclaurin of M.I.T., who, in 1950, entered into a series of informal discussions with Joseph F. Kelly, a Massachusetts contractor, and with me. Our main topics of conversation were something as follows:

The movement of populations away from the center to the outskirts of cities, as previously mentioned, brings them eventually to undeveloped, rural land, and to the opportunity of housing themselves better, more spaciously, than ever before. But the traditional process of land development works against the opportunity because the individual entrepreneur, the land developer, has to undertake heavy initial expenses in building road and water systems before he can complete his houses, and even, in most cases, before he has any sure prospect of selling them. (It's important to note that undeveloped land itself generally comes cheap.) And so, wanting to minimize his beginning expenses—and conscious always of the hazards and calamities of his trade—the prudent developer keeps his roads and water lines short, and divides the land up into lots as small as the law allows. Since a conventional house goes up best on level ground, he will use his heavy road-making equipment to scrape it flat, and in order to permit his trucks and workmen free access to the scenes of creation, he will root out and bash down all the trees that stand in the way. And since topsoil brings a good price, quite often he will skim *that* off, and sell it elsewhere. All of this is a straight-on approach to the business of making houses for people and an honest profit at the same time. In a way, perhaps, it repays nature for the hardships she inflicted on our ancestors, but it is a rough justice. (Take, for instance, the peninsula region in California, south of San Francisco, where some of the most beautiful land in this country is being rolled out and cut up like a sheet of cookies.)

What are some of the ways in which the process may be improved? Not by building codes, most likely. One answer would be a strict, regional planning—control of land development by local or state authority—but it's not one to which we easily resort. Another, and the one which engaged the interest of Maclaurin, Kelly, and me, would consist in the development of land by a private organization of house buyers, who, as a group, would finance the entire process, according to plans they had agreed on. They would thus buy themselves land, trees, and space at a low price in return for an early commitment, a longer wait than usual, and acceptance of some of the uncertainties which the individual developer must usually bear by himself.

There are many ways, obviously, in which such an organization may set itself up. A housing cooperative is one. This is a system we fancied at the outset, since, in a cooperative setup, buyers may begin with a smaller stake, and apply for forty-year rather than the usual twenty-year mortgages. As it worked out, we found the regulations governing cooperatives splendidly complex and, for the kind of building we had in mind, without workable precedent. (Though, for these reasons, we abandoned the approach, it may yet offer good opportunities.)

Conantum was undertaken, as I remember, after Kelly's observation that we might talk about land developments indefinitely; the thing was to *try* one. The idea was persuasive. Maclaurin would act as sponsor, underwriting initial expenses; Fritz, Leon, and I would act as planners and architects, and Kelly as the executive builder. The place we chose for the purpose was a 195-acre tract of woodland—hills, pines, and meadows—along the Sudbury River in Concord. ("Conantum" is an old name for this and the neighboring areas; there are some references in Thoreau.)

The way in which this land might typically have been developed was this:

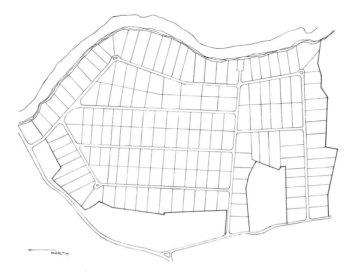

We proposed to divide it up into 104 lots, like this:

Forty acres of ground were set aside as "common land," following a system devised on a much smaller scale in the Snake Hill community. This was to be, and is, owned by the group, open to all, and used by them for playgrounds, ball fields, tennis courts, skating rinks, boat landings, or whatever else they might decide. The area as a whole is safe from encroachment and from heavy traffic. The sizes of 104 building lots, as drawn, range from one to several acres. Thirty of the lots border on common land. The advantages for families— particularly for children—are obvious. To each buyer, the cost of his land, the roads and water to serve it, and an undivided share in the common land was an average of twenty-nine hundred dollars.

Since the project had begun at M.I.T., though not under its auspices, our initial group of buyers ran heavily to engineers—electrical, aeronautical, mechanical, and sanitary —together with a few maverick social scientists, a brace of psychiatrists, mathematicians, architects, a smattering of lawyers, and one aspiring milkman. As a group they were hard-headed and vocal. When it came to the business of construction, on every point—the mixture of concrete, soil mechanics as related to the building of septic tanks, or the wiring of base plugs—the group included someone better, more scientifically informed than Maclaurin or Kelly or me. And this, at times, proved a mixed blessing.

Fritz, Leon, and I, together with Margaret Ross (who had dropped into our office looking for a weekend's work, and has never since been relinquished), turned to the business of designing the houses for Conantum. As in the case of Snake Hill, they were not to be prefabricated, but to be designed on a standard basis, pre-cut on site, and built operatively and inexpensively. In this latter consideration we had something to go on. Leon had recently built himself a house in Lexington, three stories high, at a cost which was about half as much per square foot as the typical custom house. The ways in which he had saved his money were various. They originated mainly from his remarkably close knowledge of building supplies and processes. He determined on a simple shape—the classic "house shape" in fact, with a pitched roof and four straight outside walls. He planned it so that it might be built on a slope with a livable first floor/basement, of which one side was mostly window. The dimensions of his roof and rooms were determined no more on aesthetic principles than by the question of what sizes of lumber were available, and could be used without cutting or waste. The gable ends of the house were mostly glass; this made the third story, under the roof, bright and usable, without cutting the roof line for dormers. All his double-hung window units were of the same size. Most structural members were planned so as to require no finish, and to act as trim. And so on.

Leon had run head-on against one of the tenets of enlightened architecture. He had not designed his house to "fit the land," which, as an enlightened architect, he always did for our clients. He had designed the most economical house he could think of—and then looked around for land to fit it onto. When we chided him for this, his answer was simple: he needed a good big house, and this was the way he could afford it.

One advantage of a Lipshutz-style house for Conantum was that it could be modified

Three of a variety of plans
possible in interior arrangement
of the Conantum House

to fit almost any slope of land. Another, a matter of fashion, was that when fitted into a slope, in spite of its two or three levels of height, it offered a fairly low profile. The height was necessary. This is the only way to get space into a house at low cost—to "stack" it. But in the last fifteen years or so, the public's darling has been the low-level, ranch-on-a-slab house, despite the fact that in cool climates its foundation costs are disproportionate.

By February of 1951, Maclaurin had completed arrangements to purchase the land, and recruited a list of ninety potential buyers. The schedule on which we were proceeding called hopefully for the completion of all preliminaries by March fifteenth—house design, the signing of sales agreements, and approval of our road and water plans by Concord. Construction of road and water systems was to begin then, the first house was to start on April fifteenth, and the whole works to be complete by early September of 1951. I know that was the schedule because we wrote it down.

The business of house design went well enough. Taking the Lipshutz house as a starting point, and using the same kinds and dimensions of material, we found it possible to offer a considerable variety of plans. There were two basic frame sizes—24 by 32 and 24 by 40— and length could be added to these in multiples of five feet. Each house could be built with a finished or unfinished attic, or finished or unfinished basement—or both—or neither. ("Attic" and "basement," in this case, are misleading terms—both were designed for use as good living space. The basement, for example, built on a sloping lot, would be above grade

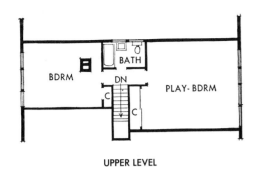

UPPER LEVEL

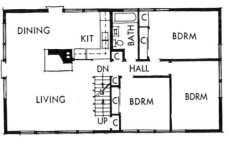

MAIN FLOOR

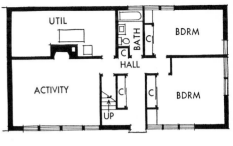

LOWER LEVEL

on at least two sides, and opened out by windows.) The 24-by-40 house could be built with either two or three bedrooms on the main floor. Each one of the houses, moreover, could be "flipped," allowing for further variety. We were also able to offer innumerable small variations in the placement of doors and windows; in the substitution of floor-to-ceiling glass for solid walls (or vice versa); in surfacing materials, inside and out; and the like. So that our buyers had a choice—depending on how you figure—of from nine to seventy-two substantially different dwellings, from a minimum of four rooms to a maximum of eight or nine.

This variety of design, I think, was a good accomplishment. But considered with what followed after, it may have been our first, fatal glass of beer. Because our buyers, among them, chose something like forty different models. And the work crews who were later assembled to build them were never quite reconciled to the fact that one house was usually a little different from the next and that they had to read the plans to find out how. The degree of their confusion was not great—but the houses were priced too low to permit *any*.

It was intentional from the start, of course, that the costs be held as low as possible, and when Mr. Kelly's staff took over the plans, to make the building estimate, they proceeded on that basis. The estimates they arrived at were surprising, even by comparison to the original Lipshutz model. $8,650 would buy the smallest, two-bedroom house. $12,385 would buy the larger frame house, with a finished second floor (three bedrooms, living room, dining area, kitchen, and bath downstairs; two bedrooms and bath up). $11,210 would buy the larger two-bedroom model, with attic and basement unfinished. $16,895 would buy the three-bedroom model with both finished second floor and finished basement—nine rooms, two baths. And so on.

The wise entrepreneur, at this point, would have regarded the difference between the cost price of his houses and the amount he could expect to sell them for—and treated himself to a 20 per cent markup. But this project had set out differently, and we stuck to the estimates. Only the trouble here was that, since plans for a "cooperative," open-end approach had fallen through, from the outset we were dealing with our buyers on a conventional, fixed-price basis. At the same time that, as developers, we accepted the hazards of upset costs, we sacrificed the developer's privilege of writing them, later on, into a final house price.

An additional complication, fairly early in the proceedings, was that, in the press of his own work, it proved impossible for Mr. Kelly himself to continue as builder. A system was devised whereby he lent a production manager from his office, Mr. Thomas O'Donnell, and Mr. O'Donnell was backed by Fritz Day from ours. Fritz's position was ambiguous. Beyond the drawing of plans, the architect's traditional sole responsibility is that of supervision—making periodic inspections, as client's representative, to ensure that plans and specifications have been met—and not getting involved in the process of building itself. On the other hand, work was going forward, and *someone* had to help steer it. So Fritz, for sev-

eral months, was catching the brickbats from both sides. And from his senior associate at that; I had chosen two of the lots, and a house, and was a buyer myself.

Construction of road and water systems began, actually, in mid-May, and construction of houses in July. By now our group of buyers had begun to show some signs of impatience. They had floundered through the winter snow to examine their land, picnicked there throughout the spring, tied rags around the trees they especially wanted preserved (including a few in the middle of what was charted to become roadway), held meetings, organized themselves into a number of committees, and now they wanted something to happen. To deal with them, in the aggregate and individually, was educational. It is hard to say which is more rigorous: the formal written complaint of a buyers' inspection committee, or the wife of an assistant professor out to avenge a juniper bush.

By mid-August, eighty lots had been cleared, sixty-five excavations dug, and seventeen foundations poured. Full crews were in the field, but the delivery date of September fifteenth was being revised into the future. The buyers as a whole remained cheerful. The attitude of their various committees became a trifle firm. I remember particularly the work of the committee on construction and inspection. They were mostly engineers, as noted, with precise knowledge of details of the work, and means and equipment to test it out. On one occasion, during the foundation work, the committee arrived with a slump cone to test the quality of the concrete mix. While the committee and the workmen stood round about, one member filled the cone and debouched it onto a board—where it subsided into a wide gray puddle. The results of that test were brought to us swiftly—first by the buyers' committee, and then, over the phone, by the driver of the cement truck. The driver was aggrieved. In the first place, he said, if he allowed the cement to become thick enough to pass the slump test, it would be a little too stiff to pour out of the mixer. In the second place, he wasn't going to make another delivery while those damn scientists were poking around, and what did we say to that? Nothing.

On another occasion the inspection committee came with a moisture meter to determine the water content of the lumber. ("Framing lumber shall be well-seasoned #2 grade hemlock, or Douglas fir . . .") After inserting the meter into a number of two-by-fours, and obtaining a variety of discrepant readings from it, in the spirit of true science they drove it into a living pine at the corner of one lot, and achieved the dryest reading of all.

After all was said and done, the quality of materials and workmanship was good. In the opinion of a consultant called in by the buyers, the Conantum houses were superior to most speculative building, and average for custom building. The only trouble was that it kept taking too long to make them that way. Work had been let out to a variety of subcontractors. And contractors, as is well known, come in all shapes and sizes. Some followed the plans with care. Others did for one house just as they had done for the one before—and hoped it would all work out right. (There was the case of one buyer who stood off—with a shovel—

the cement crew who wanted to pour his slab before the ductwork had gone in.) And while the variations from house to house were essentially simple, in every house, at one time or another, it was needful to go back and do major work over, simply because some workman had omitted to read plans. Fritz, who had been used to work on individual houses with individual, hand-picked builders, could never quite reconcile himself to the crew leader who would listen in silence to a long, careful explanation of some point, nod soberly, and go off to do it wrong. We could, and should, have hired a larger supervisory force. But that would be spending money to save money, and we were still hopeful that things would begin to go righter.

One thing that went well was the arrival on the scene of Ed Diehl. Ed is a Pennsylvania Dutchman, a graduate engineer and architect, of round, deceptively innocent countenance, and a frame size which varies from plump to meager, depending on his attitude of mind. He came to Conantum in the guise of an interior decorator, and was soon recruited as an ambulatory straw boss, touring the project to check on specifications, heartening the faint, and chivvying the laggard from their long noonday meals under the cool trees.

But the pace of things remained somewhat too leisurely. Costs were creeping up, and there were a full quota of unrewarding incidents. I recall the night watchman, a retired policeman, who was hired to stop petty thievery from the project. By the time he was apprehended, several months later, he had trucked away several thousand dollars' worth of supplies, and disposed of them at a clear profit. Another case, less grave but more typical, was that of the bulldozer operator, who backed over and broke a foundation wall—at exactly the moment that he heard the firm, approaching tread of the inspection committee. Panic-stricken, he dismounted from his vehicle, its engine still running, and fled off through the woods and home.

By the middle of November, two months after the originally scheduled completion date, the Conantum roads had been graded and graveled, but not surfaced, the water system was still twelve hundred feet short of completion, eighty-five foundations had been poured, seventy-five houses had been framed and boarded, but the weather was turning cold. We were faced with the question of whether to pursue work through the winter, or to lash things down and wait for spring to come again. Here we made our main wrong choice. Our motivations were a desire to get it over with and a sense of responsibility to our buyers, many of whom were migrating from apartment to apartment in the city, with no sure place to go. At any rate we decided to keep on with things. The snows descended. Expenses met and passed them on the way. By the sixth of February the water system was complete, and eight families had moved in. By March fifteenth, about fifty families were in, and most of the other houses nearly finished. By the twenty-third of April, Conantum was broke.

The next few weeks were distressful but not disastrous. Sixty of the houses were substantially complete and being lived in, though precious few were finished to the last floor tile or light fixture. Worst off was the buyer who was left with a large hole in the middle of his lot, a few lengths of pipe, and nothing else; others stood somewhere in between. The heavy losers included some of the contractors, who deserved a better fate; three of the buyers, who had made a private loan to Conantum; Carl Koch & Associates; and Rupert Maclaurin.

Maclaurin had hoped to make a small profit from the sale of the land, of which he was the original purchaser; that hope had gone glimmering. But from the start, intentionally, the Conantum venture had operated on a small margin, and he felt a strong Scotch determination to carry it through. On May sixth he offered fifty thousand dollars to the receiver, to buy things as they stood. The offer was formally accepted on May twenty-third. Work began again on May twenty-sixth, and the last of the houses were finished by late fall. And the buyers, among themselves, began a subscription of cash toward repaying the three who had made the earlier loan.

In the six years since, Conantum has settled in as part of Concord. Its road and water systems have been taken over by the town, in usual fashion. There are only a few reminders of its once separate entity: the fact that the houses go together, the sinewy recollections of its inhabitants, and the area of common land, to which, year by year, more facilities are added—the gravel pit has become a ski slope, one field is planted with tennis courts, another is graded and grassed into a huge ball field and playground. The marks of construction are covered over by pine needles and moss. For trees taken out, new ones are growing. It is still rolling woodland, as it began.

But there are still, I think, some characteristics, in the relation of people, houses, and land, which mark this off from many developments. The involvement of the buyers' group from the beginning in the processes of planning and construction, whatever the rigors it occasioned along the way, still continues in the active attitude they take toward the use of their homes and land. It is partly a matter of rooms being added on, garages built, and terraces and gardens laid out—building, in fact, seems never quite to have stopped. These are the obvious manifestations. But what is still more rewarding, from an architectural point of view, is that, with space enough, all of the different things manage to "fit": the formal garden next door to the woodpile, the well-kept lawn next to the stone wall that was heaped up a hundred years before. It is still fascinating to me to take a drive through Conantum every couple of months to note these changes. I feel particularly pleased at the individuality which so many of the owners have shown in planting, developing, and adding to their houses. All but a few have really improved what they started with, some with professional help, some just by adopting parts of the features of their neighbors' houses and gardens with some original interpretations of their own to suit their particular needs and land.

Year by year a few of the residents sell, and move off to jobs in other parts. (And sell, it should be noted, at a considerable profit.) But not many. Others go, and then return. Some are determined to stay on regardless, according to their own evaluation of what money will or won't buy. It is a satisfying place to live.

8 The House That Techbuilt

In 1953 came the Techbuilt house. And our ten-year record of mishap, rude practical education, and artistic successes qualified by insolvency was spotted unexpectedly by something that worked—and worked well. While this was what we had been searching for, after all, I can only look back with interest at the scope and suddenness of it. One model of a house, first planned in spare time, fabricated in an overgrown carpentry shop in Acton, Massachusetts, built speculatively in West Concord, varied and built again in Weston, turned into twenty-two models of house, a corporation, four factories, and a system of ninety franchised builder-dealers from New York to California. By the end of 1957, Techbuilts had been put up by ones, twos, and small communities in thirty-two separate states.

Into all this—the design and marketing of the Techbuilt—have gone a measure of simple logic, some weight of experience from preceding ventures, and a generous share of good luck.

As to its design, first of all:

In some respects, the Techbuilt derives from the Conantum house, as the Conantum did from the Lipshutz house. This applies most visibly to the simplicity of its shape, the "stacking" of space, the pitched roof, and the wide use of glass at the gable ends. But there is another, modified inheritance. The Conantum houses were offered with livable basements, livable attics, both or neither (only 3 out of 108 buyers chose neither). And one of the clearest lessons from Conantum was that these attics and basements were immensely less expensive to build than the main floors of the houses. To add a basement—above grade on one or two sides, tight, dry, and fully windowed—cost about $1,200 unfinished or $4,500 finished. An attic—space for two rooms, bath, and storage—added about $800 unfinished, $2,700 finished. And so, to make a simple-minded inference, a finished two-story house, consisting of an attic, a basement, and *no* main floor, should cost $7,200. And this precisely, innocently, was what we set out to design.

Now the figures given, of course, represent marginal cost: what it takes to add onto something which was going to be built *anyway*. And yet, in our effort to subtract, or rather, make full use of, the "anyway" parts of the house, there was, and is, a kind of primitive sense. It goes like this:

In most parts of the country, the matter of putting a house *up* first of all involves digging *down* (below frost line to a depth, in New England in any case, of three or four feet), and then building or pouring a vertical concrete foundation wall, and covering it all up again.

But if, in any event, you have to dig, it adds very little in effort and expense to scoop out the whole works, and use the foundation wall actually to enclose living space. (You don't have to dig down so far, in fact, because what comes out of the inside can be graded up around the outside. It is a pushing-around rather than a gouging operation, allows for lighter, less expensive equipment, and is easier on the land.) And if—to continue—the area you have scooped out and enclosed is set into a slope of land and opens out above grade, as in the Conantum and Lipshutz houses, the result is something like this: (The purist will note that there is still some trenching involved, for the lower foundation.)

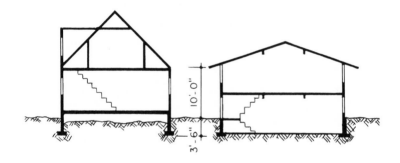

Left, **conventional house and foundation;** *right,* **Techbuilt foundation**

The inside of the foundation can be clad, finished, and floored like any room, so as to hide the cement. And it can be windowed anywhere, as well as at the gable ends. So that to call this space a "basement" is a matter of terminology, convenient but perhaps misleading. It bears no resemblance, even in passing, to the conventional basement—damp, cold, and moldering—a last resting place for steamer trunks and heads of moose.

The same holds true with respect to the attic. The traditional attic is mostly waste—

a triangular space, airless, hot, high enough to stand in below the peak, and to crawl around in, poking at hornets' nests, at the eaves.

But this area, like that inside the foundation, can be made usable—simply by hoisting it five or six feet at the sides, and windowing it correctly. Ceiling height at the peak then becomes ten feet or so. It offers as much space, usable and "feelable," as any shape of room.

And so the house—attic on basement—comes to look like this (seen from the gable end):

Ben Schnall

It seems well here to mention some smaller considerations which developed in the course of planning the Techbuilt and which are difficult to show in diagram form. One is that either door—the one shown, or the one located midway of the side—may be used for the main entrance, depending on how the house is sited to the street. Another is that the entrance of the stairway to the second floor is "central": it gives access to any room without passage through another. A third is that, for reasons of economy and to maintain the flexibility of inside space, utilities and immovable fixtures like stairs, chimney, and bath are located in the core. A fourth is that since the plans, like those of Conantum, can be flipped or mirror-imaged, the house can be sited to take full advantage of the land. (In most cases this means the situation of the gable-end windows toward the south or east, but it depends, as with all houses, on the desire for view or the need for privacy. The windows are important: they give the house a remarkable sense of freedom, and extension onto the land. When the house is located in the city, as it has been many times over, privacy has to come by way of screening, terracing, or fencing.)

The ten-foot outside wall of the Techbuilt is little higher than that of the conventional one-story house, so that by putting attic on basement, within the same height and perimeter and with only slightly greater use of material, living space is effectively doubled. And we found —adding to this conception the economies which had already been planned into the Conantum and Lipshutz houses—that we could build at $7.50 a square foot. The conventional builder's house, at that time, cost about \$10, and a custom-built house about \$15, a square foot. (All figures have risen since, and vary by locality.)

The foregoing is not the "total conception" of the Techbuilt house. (There remain a number of architectural small points concerning the mode of its framing, and so on.) Nor did its planning go in just that order. Nor was it something we undertook with simple good cheer. This, unlike Conantum, would represent a deliberate choice by us, as architects, to function also as builders. Fritz was still tending blisters from the Conantum experience, and looked with a cool, hard eye on the first sketches. But we inched ahead, acquired a piece of land, hired back Ed Diehl to clamp down on the pricing and construction, cleaned out the till, and completed the first Techbuilt house in March of 1953. It sold handily enough, and roused the usual polite interest from fellow architects, relatives, and the editors of home magazines. By fall we had six or seven more under way, all bespoken.

The Conantum houses had been pre-cut, but not pre-built to any considerable extent. These new ones were. The first set a pattern which has been followed, in the main, ever since. The method of prefabrication and erection is as follows:

The shell of the house—walls, roof, and second floor—is constructed of panels on a four-foot-wide module (the largest, the roof panels, are fourteen feet long). As with the Acorn House, the construction of panels is stressed skin, though of more conventional materials—plywood sheets bonded to wooden framing members. (The strength of the panels is worth remarking.

In one test a consultant engineer chose three at random, laid them across sawhorses, and started piling cement blocks on their middles. The first gave way, having bent two inches, under a total weight of five and three-quarters tons.) Windows and doors are constructed on the same module as the solid panels, which allows for the usual variations of assembly.

The making of panels of this type and size saves little in cost as compared with conventional framing. But the advantages multiply when it comes to erection. A single truckload delivers the shell of the house. Unloaded, it looks like this:

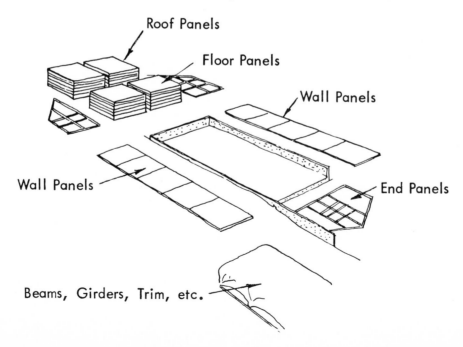

Roof Panels

Floor Panels

Wall Panels

Wall Panels

End Panels

Beams, Girders, Trim, etc.

The virtue of the particular size and lightness of panels is that two men, in a pinch, can unload and frame the house by themselves. Four are better—two rough carpenters and two laborers, working together, without special equipment, can set up the shell and roof it over in two days' time. The work of the different trades—masons, plumbers, electricians— then goes forward *indoors,* out of the weather.

Side walls and one gable end of the house are first framed, spiked, and bolted together. The remaining gable end remains open until the second-floor panels have been placed.

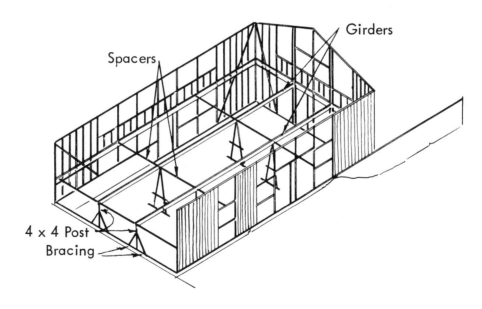

The weight of the second floor, and later the roof, is borne by wooden carrying beams—usually 4 by 10 inches—which run the entire length of the house, and beyond; and by the steel columns or posts which support the beams. After the two sides and one end are up, beams are placed and propped, the second-floor panels are slid along them into place and secured. Then the remaining gable end is closed up, the roof beams are placed, the roof panels lifted up, on, and fastened. It is very nearly as simple as that, and so is the progression of finish work which remains. (As with any house, the variety of alternative finishing materials, inside and outside, is unlimited.)

Since the weight of the house is borne by the outside walls, beams, and columns, this means that the space inside can be divided up in a number of different ways to suit the needs of individual families, and to accommodate to the ways in which their needs may change over time. Structural additions to houses are expensive; it's better to have the space *inside* to start with, unfinished if need be, and develop it by plan.

It was obvious from the beginning that in its depth of simplicity and its neatness, the Techbuilt might offer do-it-yourself possibilities to the family who were short on cash but long on ambition and tolerably handy with tools. A builder could do it more quickly and with greater elegance, but it seemed worthy to us to prepare a manual of instructions for potential buyers, and it seemed that, for those who were pleased by it, the "idea" of the house

Ben Schnall

Exteriors of two Techbuilt Houses

Ben Schnall

Interiors of two Techbuilt Houses

Lionel Freedman

was perhaps as valuable as anything else we could offer. The conviction persists and has been of some profit to many.

When we began the first house, we incorporated. It was at that time that we settled on "Techbuilt" as an over-all title for the enterprise, the house, and the idea, feeling that it had pleasant connotations of technique, or machine-like precision. The name has never been entirely satisfactory. For one thing, people keep trying to leave out the "U." For another, it has been an embarrassment to M.I.T., from time to time, in seeming to imply paternity— a wicked suggestion, if one considers the age and piety of that institution. But by the time we really wanted to change it, too many things had already happened.

One was that we were discovered by television. By *Excursion*—a half-hour show for young people, developed by the Ford Foundation TV-Radio Workshop, in 1954, as a companion series to *Omnibus*. *Excursion* undertook to show all the main events of planning and building a house (a Techbuilt, redesigned actually into a new *Excursion* model), from the first visit to the empty lot (in Weston, Massachusetts), until the time the house was finished, furnished, and ready to be lived in. According to our assignment from Excursion, we were to turn the trick at a cost-to-customer of $14,000—not including the price of land or furniture—finishing the first floor complete and half-finishing the second. Then we were to demonstrate two different methods of furnishing it: the first a fifteen-hundred-dollar solution, making use of plywood-door tables, sling chairs, and the like; and the second a sky-the-limit arrangement of inlaid coffee wagons, block-printed drapes, and whatever.

The film was directed by Willard Van Dyke, narrated by Burgess Meredith, and mounted on two successive *Excursion* shows in February of 1954. We, for our part, were vaguely aware that television was a potent medium, and had made some preliminary arrangements to welcome any interest which might be stirred—making reprints of a magazine article on the house, and planting a few road signs on the highways around Weston. (Ed Diehl, discovering some paper apple blossoms in the five-and-ten, bought a couple of dozen, and tied them thoughtfully on the winter-bare trees which overhung the terrace.) It seemed reasonable to expect visitors.

The broadcasts were watched by something like twenty million people. A sizable proportion—or so it seemed—promptly got in their cars and drove over to have a look. On the approaching roads, for three weekends, were five miles of nearly stationary traffic, with spectacular snarls at all the intersections. The police were understandably sore, but there was no way to take the house and hide it somewhere. The happy citizen armies tramped in from all sides, churning the terraces into seas of mud, milling up and down the stairs, unscrewing light bulbs for mementos, gazing raptly at the cork tile, and turning the stove on and off. In the middle of it all stood Ed Diehl, revolving slowly, wearing the tiny smile which represents his closest approach to rapture, and answering questions—"Yes, ma'am, the faucets contain real water."

Within the space of a few days the Techbuilt had become as well known as any house in America. It was a good house; we knew that. So were those we had designed before. And peope had liked those others—but not millions of people and all at once. Opportunity, it was clear, had not hesitated at the door; it came lurching inside and gathered us all in its sweaty embrace. We looked uncertainly at each other and wondered just what to do about it.

9 . . . And How It Grew

One of the first things we had to do, obviously, was to raise money. Ours was a curious variant of the usual commercial pattern: we had a product, and a hearty demand from consumers, but no handy way of getting *it* to *them*. Even before the *Excursion* program, we had had some hopes of expanding in gradual, orderly fashion from the Boston area throughout New England. But now we had hopeful builders flying in to see us from places like Michigan and California, and letters from Hawaii.

In September of 1954, we reincorporated, into Techbuilt Homes, Inc., and made a successful public sale of 120,000 shares of stock. Even before this, we had begun to arrange for manufacture of components in different central areas, and to issue franchises to builders.

The builders who came to see us were an agglomeration of types—old pros and young visionaries, responsible architects, and talented freeloaders. To winnow them out was a hard responsibility. Our first major embarrassment came when, on the same day but unbeknownst to each other, two different applicants, Keith Gilchrist and Leonard Wolfe, arrived from the same city of Detroit. Clearly, it seemed, the politic thing to do was keep them hidden from each other, and Ed Diehl spent a haggard morning, leading them up and down different flights of stairs in our tiny headquarters, ushering them into different rooms, and commuting from one to the other with fresh piles of descriptive literature. (What made it worse was that, on a first acquaintance, Gilchrist looked a good deal like Wolfe, and vice versa—both young, hard-jawed, wearing glasses, etc.) By midafternoon, as things went, Gilchrist had tired of the strangely intermittent conversation and invited Ed out for a few undisturbed drinks. When they returned, Ed left Gilchrist under the guard of an affable secretary, and reported to Wolfe—who by now was weary of reading pamphlets, and invited Ed out to talk about things over drinks. Ed accepted, unsteady but game.

It was around six when they came back. By now, their host was sure of just one thing—he wasn't going to eat two separate dinners. He flung open the intervening door and, slurring his consonants a bit, made introductions. Messrs. Gilchrist and Wolfe regarded each other coldly, and stepped outside. Next day they reappeared—and announced their intention of taking the franchise *together*. They did, and put the first Techbuilt in the Midwest, and have been at it ever since.

The manufacturing and distribution system established by Techbuilt was different from that of the majority of prefabricators. We had neither means nor desire to set up a single factory, make and gather parts for the house all in one spot, and ship from there to anywhere. Instead we arranged for the fabrication of the Techbuilt shell and panels, according to specification, by producers in Acton (Acorn Houses, Inc.), Huntington, Long Island (Bush Prefabricated Structures, Inc.), and later in Urbana, Illinois (Creative Buildings, Inc.), and Whittier, California (Structural Prefabricators, Inc.). That part of the package was shipped by these producers direct to the builder-dealers. Other parts—pre-hung doors and the like, bought by Techbuilt on a volume basis—were shipped to the builder through the makers' regular channels of distribution, so that Techbuilt came, not so much a "package," properly speaking, as a system of converging components. The builder, having purchased these basic components, went on to complete the house at his own discretion—choosing the land to put it on, providing exterior and interior finish materials, plumbing, heating, clos-etry, finished floors, and so on—and to determine the final sale price.

The system has had its obvious advantages and disadvantages—some will follow— and some modifications since. But it enabled us, uniquely among prefabricators, to set up a nationwide, network operation, however loose-jointedly. By the time of our stock issue, we had granted twenty-one builder franchises, and eighty houses were complete or under way —in places like New Haven and Schenectady, and farther out in Cleveland, Chicago, and St. Louis. The first in the Midwest—Gilchrist and Wolfe's—attracted fifty thousand visitors. Techbuilt was continuing to get a good press, and even some attention from abroad. *"Cual es el sentido de una casa de dos pisos—y he aqui el nuevo tip de casa de dos pisos.* Techbuilt." (De Carlos Koch.) And the house was winning a good share of national awards.

The reasons for immediate public acceptance of Techbuilt, keeping in mind some of the topics of earlier chapters, seem fairly clear. Its outward appearance—pitched roof, simple rectangular shape, low profile—was somewhat reminiscent of "traditional" architecture, what people were used to. It could fit into any neighborhood of houses without stirring up deep antipathies. (This was happy circumstance, not a factor in our original design of the house. If a flat roof or a cucumber shape had offered better service, we would have planned it like that. We weren't out to preserve the best of all periods.) The materials of which the house was made—unlike, for instance, those used in the Acorn—were familiar and available. In structure it was conformable to the provisions of most building codes, however antiquated. (In fact, our use of a modular, four-foot size of panel resulted in a surplus of about twenty studs per house.) Our system of production lent itself to decentralization, avoided heavy investment in plant, and permitted our use of purchasing power over long periods rather than in heavy, volume commitments at single times. We did not, and have not, emerged scatheless on all counts, but these considerations help to explain why our difficulties have tended to come one by one and not, as for many others, in a decisive knot. Though Techbuilt has both gained and lost money—and is *still* technically in the red—it shows no signs of the early doom which is supposed to overtake the virtuous and beautiful.

The history of Techbuilt from 1954 to the present demonstrates an interesting mixture of purposes. On the one hand, for example, we have wanted to design houses, and parts of houses, in the best way we know, without cluttering them with odds and ends of "selling points." On the other hand, obviously, we have wanted them to sell. We have wanted always to develop each design to its limits, to explore the logic of variations upon it, and to develop

from one design to another. But this same enthusiasm of design has sometimes led us perilously close to the limits of our own capacity to produce and that of our builders to build,
and beyond any present, realistic public interest in making choices. We have wanted to
sponsor the use of new materials, to urge the acceptance of modes of architecture we know
to be practical, and aesthetic devices we know to be satisfying—to stay close to the front of
developments—but in some instances we have bumped hard against small popular dislikes,
and, as a business organization, have had to backtrack. Knowing that the house will meet
and exceed any rational building code, we have been determined not to compromise the
economy of its construction, and in some cases have had to. We have wanted to "grow" fast
and at the same time keep running expenses, and hence house prices, low. We have wanted
to assist our builders in the planning of communities which make generous use of land and
in which the selling price of houses is kept to a minimum, and at the same time not interfere
with their natural inclinations to build in the way they think they can sell. We have wanted
to, and have, increased the size of the Techbuilt "package" without infringing on the dealer
or buyer's option to vary some things to suit himself. We have wanted to encourage the
building of the houses by individuals on a do-it-yourself basis, and have spent long hours
comforting inspired amateurs over the fact that the house won't fit on a foundation nine inches
wider at one end than the other. We have wanted to act as a stimulus and source of ideas to

the building industry, but without having every pirate who owns a tape measure copy what he can see of Techbuilt and sell it for his own.

The desire to be a good designer, or producer, or builder, is not always easy to reconcile with the craving to eat off bone china and ride a yacht to work, even when the compromises involved might seem to consist in just giving people what they are willing to think they want. The most difficult part of all is to determine on a progress of things which will always keep intact the essential qualities with which they began. On that point, concerning Techbuilt, I remain well content.

Some examples:

We might have had a good thing of it if we had concentrated at first on producing and selling just one house—the *Excursion* type, already popular—as a sort of Model A of the prefabrication industry. The making of architectural plans and variations is an irksome and expensive business. But a modular system of construction, and the system we had adopted of weight bearing and interior flexibility, made other models logically desirable—as well as the idea of Techbuilt communities planned to allow individual families individual choice of dwelling. By the end of 1954, we had seven different models in hand, and there have been a number since.

In 1956, we added a series of one-story models. This, indeed, was in answer to customer demand—mostly from the level Midwest. In dollar per square foot, obviously, the one-story could not offer as great economies as the two-story. In versatility, we planned it to offer more. It was designed actually in halves; the "living area" of living room, kitchen, and dining space being differentiated from the "quiet area" of bedrooms and bath, and the two halves being connected by a room-link entryway. There were four different choices of living areas, and four different bedroom and bath arrangements—sixteen possible combinations. The two halves, moreover, could be built in line, offset to one side or the other, or set actually at right angles, or, of course, built "flipped." To top it off, depending on the site, either living or bedroom area could be built over a Techbuilt basement—bringing it back, more or less, to the two-story idea.

We were well pleased with this variety of choice. But the hard fact, as it turned out, was that some of the possible combinations were more expensive to build than they had any right to be from plan. And that the wealth of choice, to the prospective buyer, was as apt to be as confusing as stimulating. You will sell as many houses offering six varieties as sixteen, and you will not have spent thousands of dollars on plans which ravish no soul but your own. At some future time, it's likely that we will want to restore the full choice of one-story models; at the present writing, the variety is less profuse.

This was one instance when our enthusiasm as designers led us to offer more than our buyers were inclined to make use of. Another case—of a different order—was that of the Techbuilt Spacemaking Furniture. The design of this furniture, actually, antedated the

Photographs by Alderman Studios

**Here, and on the following page,
are four examples of Techbuilt
Spacemaking Furniture components**

Photographs by Alderman Studios

house. It had begun from our participation in a Museum of Modern Art competition in 1947, and it was stimulated further by our dealers' requests that we design a set of freestanding wardrobe closets to go with the house. We discovered, going by modules, that the same general components could be worked into twenty-one different, basic pieces of furniture—not only closets but chests, shelves, room dividers, and desks. We designed these pieces of furniture to be shipped "knocked down," and assembled with nothing more complicated than a screwdriver. All units of one-foot depth could be hitched together with any and all others, and one-foot units could be fastened to the two-footers by way of a divider unit. The buyer could choose and arrange the furniture for himself, change it around as the mood took him, start with one or two units, and add on others over a period of time. The furniture was made of Philippine mahogany (light textured); would fit other houses than Techbuilt, and could be arranged into the Techbuilt in umpteen different ways. A triumph. But we tried having it made by two different producers, and they made it very badly indeed, and it cost too much. And now, for the time being, we are back to the wardrobe closets.

Other ventures, more successful, were the introduction of Techbuilt carports, garages, and vacation cottages. The cottage might be taken as an example of the occasions when extension of design did pay off. We planned it in two sizes—16 by 24 and 20 by 24—and then, while we were at it, planned two larger sizes—24 by 24 and 24 by 28—contrary to expert sales advice and without really expecting them to sell much. The larger sizes have sold extraordinarily well, and the smaller ones hardly at all.

Our desire to introduce the public to new taste treats has led us into occasional mischances—as with the red-cedar clapboard. There was a time when we were promoting red-cedar clapboard as a finish material for the inside wall. To us its advantages were conclusive: it was easy to apply, required no paint, was easy to maintain—and moth repellent, when you came to that. Above all, it made a warm and beautiful surface.

But what we found out was that to some people—lots of them—red-cedar clapboard was an *outside* finish material. They were willing to admit that it made sense inside and even, in fact, that it looked pretty good, and might suit some folks just dandy. But not, by golly, *them*. It seemed to us a point worth fighting, but not dying, for; we widened the choice of interior finishes.

Another point on which we have, to our mind, retreated: The one provision of local building codes which we found to recur, and with which we tangled most consistently, was that governing the size and allowable span of roof rafters. For a conventionally framed house of the same dimensions as the Techbuilt, the required size of rafter is 2 by 6 inches. In the Techbuilt we were using 2 by 4's—in a stressed-skin construction of which the load-bearing ability was perhaps eight times greater. And the roof panels, what's more, were supported midway by the carrying beams. Reason was on our side, but the dead weight of written-down

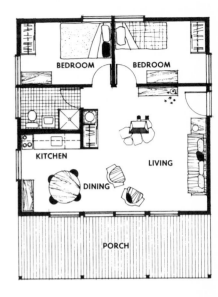

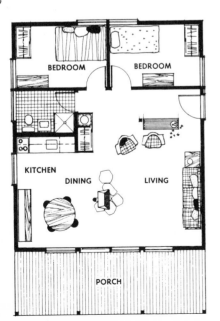

custom on the other. And now the Techbuilt roof panels are built with 2 by 6's—no longer stressed skin. Not a great matter, surely. The panels are about as easy to make as before, not more expensive, as strong as the roofs of conventional houses (though no longer stronger)—and yet the increase in bulk means that in some cases the shell of the house can't be delivered complete in one truckload. The added cost per house of such a construction change, first to last, is probably not more than a hundred or so dollars. But the endeavor to build an economical house is a battle all the way; the hundred dollarses mount up, and all of a sudden what began modestly may unravel a large bankroll.

This happened with some of the early Techbuilts. The builder—having bought the package from us, and the land to put it on from someone else, and having his choice of ways to complete the house, and wanting to make a splash—would often "tie in" with local distributors. This in turn meant using the house as a kind of showcase, for more or less fancy appliances, fixtures, finishes, and cabinetry; luxury-style air-conditioning systems; air cleansers; premium floor materials; and the like. These tie-ins are useful, often essential; they may make the difference between a modest advertisement in the newspaper and a full-page spread. But they may also make the difference of a house costing a good deal more than it might. The same situation has obtained in high-income communities where the builder can better rely on putting up the houses in ones and twos, with a considerable degree of spit and polish, than on aiming for low expense, a slimmer margin of profit, and larger quantity.

But the Techbuilt was designed to make special sense to middle-income families. One way to help the builder keep down prices, in the face of steadily rising costs, has been to increase the number of items provided, from volume, in the basic "package." We began, in 1954, by providing the shell alone—and at various later stages added in fixed and movable windows, doors, interior cabinetry, stairways, roofing materials, and—optionally—heating system, appliances, and the like. The package included, at the beginning, one quarter of the material and cost of the completed house, and includes nearly one half now, with the expectation of providing still more as time goes on.

Besides the house package itself, Techbuilt has made a point of providing builder and buyer with architectural services they would otherwise be unlikely to afford. (Though some builders like Jim Livingston, in Ann Arbor, are architects in their own right.) These include the drawing up of community plans, and assistance in the siting of individual houses on their land. In recent time this architectural service has led to the important adaptation of Techbuilt designs and material into other than single-family dwellings—the development of residences for university personnel and students, and even Techbuilt apartment houses for regular commercial *rentiers*.

Techbuilt has never been promoted as a house for the "masses"—though each year, typically, the masses become less masslike. The bulk of its sales has been to young professionals, with sizable families and unspectacular incomes (including a pleasantly high proportion of architects). Most of Techbuilt's builder-dealers make fewer than fifty "starts" a year (the fewer-than-fifty builder still accounts for more than 80 per cent of the country's building).

Techbuilts, just as any houses, have never been aesthetically foolproof. They do not lend themselves to careless building, but they have, on occasion, been unskillfully finished, or furnished, or landscaped. The simplicity of the house itself puts some responsibility on the buyer not to overstuff or overdecorate it. And since it relates to the outdoors, what happens on the land immediately around it is important, such as the care taken to preserve terrain features, and, if there is planting, the need to plant things pleasant to look *at*. All houses change as the families inside and the land outside change, the Techbuilt perhaps more than others. It begins simply. It is meant to provide the generous basis for a number of things, not the least of which is intelligent living.

Techbuilt houses have been built in steadily increasing numbers—six hundred thousand dollars' worth in 1954, double that in 1955, and double *that* in 1956, even when the tightening of mortgage credit put a deep crimp in conventional building. (At the same time there is a neat, cheerless illustration of some of the perils mentioned earlier in the fact that, for 1956, we made elaborate preparations for a *really* big year, and instead took a thorough drubbing when sales did not equal expenses.) Simple extrapolation would seem to indicate that, by 1966, Techbuilt will have a billion-dollar business. On that score, I am perhaps not so confident as I should be, but it is a satisfying thing to have helped develop, from purposes which are usually written off as academic or high-minded or theoretical, a product which can more than hold its own in a competitive market. And it is pleasant to have come upon an idea of which the value and vitality reach well beyond the series of small failures and successes of our own efforts to profit by it.

10 The Industrial House

In June of 1957, National Steel Corporation, through its subsidiary, Stran-Steel Corporation, engaged Carl Koch & Associates as consultants in planning a new approach to the field of residential building. It was the kind of opportunity for which we had been a long time waiting, it came as a natural complement to our work with Techbuilt, and once again it opened the tantalizing vision of a practical entrance by heavy industry into a market most desperately in need of it.

To be sure, large "basic" industries have been involved before now with the idea of prefabrication, as during the Depression. For years they have been in the business of supplying building components. Some of them have even marketed complete prefabricated houses, usually at a loss. What, hopefully, may distinguish National Steel's attack on the problem is, first, that it comes at a particularly ripe time, and second, that it represents a peculiarly thoughtful and open-minded approach to problems of production, architecture, and marketing.

What causes the time to be ripe? Among a number of long, poetic answers, the shortest and best, quite likely, is the estimate that, in the years between 1960 and 1975, we will be building thirty-five million new houses. But within the same period we will have enough lumber available to build just about twenty-three million—two thirds as many as we need—if we continue to build as we do today, with wood as our base material. And we will have enough *manpower* available, leaving aside the question of materials, to build perhaps one half as many as we need, if we continue to rely on tradesman-style, on-site, handicraft labor. Our only hope of getting the rest of the houses built at all consists in a marked increase in per-man productivity, and in the use of materials, besides wood, which lend themselves to volume methods: concretes, plastics, and metals—pre-eminently steel.

The invitation is unmistakable. And yet the metals industries have been invited before and have been curiously slow to accept. Today's conventional house makes use of something like one and a half tons of steel (in highly fabricated components like plumbing and heating systems, stoves, refrigerators, etc.); it could, to advantage, make use of ten or twelve tons. Part of our assignment has been to investigate all applications for steel products in the traditional builder's house. But beyond this, National is interested in looking forward to a new architecture—of which we have only seen the beginnings—which will make use of more production capacities, and of the special properties of steel, in ways and at money savings which will be extraordinary by any comparison. It is this aspect of National's approach—that it is straightforwardly a matter of experiment, search, and discovery and will do as much in the long run to "shape" the building market as it does in the short run simply to conform to it—which helps to set it apart from the routine undertakings of industry, and supplies it with some importance.

Our research, obviously, hasn't had to begin at scratch. There has been persistent experimentation through the years with applications of steel to house production, beginning with the remarkable Poulson house of 1890. And some of it has been markedly ingenious: the Suspension Steel house of 1909, the Neutra Diatom house (mast suspended, like Fuller's Dymaxion house) in 1925, a Gropius house of 1927, a Pierce Foundation House in 1932, Keck and Atwood's House of Tomorrow and Crystal House (1933, 1934), the Arcy House of 1936, and more recently Charles Eames's Case Study House in 1949, a van der Rohe design in 1955, and houses by Craig Ellwood and by William Korns in 1956. But the bulk of steel houses—like those mentioned previously, built in England in quantity after the first World War, and some built now—have tried to make use of steel simply as a kind of glorified high-performance lumber. And steel makes rather poor lumber, actually, just as it makes poor plastic or glass. In sawability, pushability, and wasteability, it cannot match the characteristics of wood. It does not lend itself to the inspired, on-the-spot improvisations for which the American carpenter is justly famous. It is a precision product of even, guaranteed performance, with the highest ratio of strength to weight of any material going. It will be only by the systematic development of uses for these attributes that steel will come to have significance for the building of the private home.

In our first, tentative research along these lines, we have asked a number of questions which will be a long time in the answering. (And it is by no means certain that one of the answers will be a new brand of prefabricated house. For steel the best bet may be the development of new, practical, structural systems and components and equipment.) But it is possible to guess ahead to some of the ways in which the characteristics of steel and steel methods will apply to, or collide with, the universe of small-house building.

It is sure, for instance, that steel framing systems can be made to offer many advantages over conventional framing in wood. One of them derives from steel's ability to *span*. In the wood-frame house, for one reason and another, width is held close to a maximum of twenty-four feet; with the use of steel members, span can be strikingly increased, and interior space kept free of supporting walls. (Flexibility of interiors, their arrangement and rearrangement, as partly foreseen in the Techbuilt house, is bound to become a distinguishing feature of our architecture in the next twenty years.) As part and parcel of this development, we will see the adaptation of steel and other materials into a growing variety of roof shapes: straight, angular, arched, and curving.

Hand in hand with these delightful prospects go a number of practical problems: How will the consumer react to the idea of a steel-framed house? (Favorably, one may suppose— but one is *just* supposing.) Who will market these steel framing members? How will they be regarded by building inspectors? At what point will their use conflict with local codes? And just *who* will assemble them into the house? This last question is likely to be the trickiest. There will be more than one nippy jurisdictional dispute—as between carpenters and metal workers—before the matter is finally resolved.

But however the arguments work out, it is quite likely that the assembly of metal parts in houses will be an extraordinarily simple matter of bolting and snapping, for the most part; and that, even within the single house, steel components will join conveniently with other materials. One of the projects on which we are engaged at this writing is the development of a system for joining a steel beam of a conventional shape into mullion frames which can receive panel sections of any rectangular shape, or—just as easily—fixed glass, or a casement or sliding window, or a door. If all goes well, the method of joining beams together will be a matter of snapping in an adapter and tightening two bolts, the gasketing and placing of a sheet of glass will be a minute's work, and the business of locking it fast will involve a few earnest whacks on a spring-steel batten, with either a rubber mallet or the heel of the hand. There is no reason why a house may not be framed, roofed, glazed, and partly or entirely sided in a day's time.

These are attributes of steel construction which should reasonably result in considerable savings in money, and a considerable gain in grace and amenity. But, as noted previously, the expense of framing a house does not bulk so large nowadays in relation to its total cost. It is the innards of houses which stand most in need of improvement—particularly their service and utilities systems, which account for about one quarter of total house cost. Steel and the other metals are already in use in these systems; here the problem is simply one of improving their use.

There are some curious aspects to the cost of the present-day bathroom: a bath-shower tub costs about $100, a sink costs about $40, and a water closet about $35—but the cost of assembling these three fixtures into a bathroom may be anywhere from $500 to $1000. Among the things which go to make up the difference are $150 worth of the plumber's personal services, his typical 60 per cent markup on pipes, fittings, and the like, and cost of the pipes themselves—a forest of them—hand-joined on site; strung up, down and around, all over the house.

As a remedy to all this, there have been a number of ventures toward the development of prefabricated mechanical cores, ranging from "plumbing-wall" arrangements to more complete assemblies, including furnace system, hot-water heater, and connections for kitchen facilities as well. The architectural usefulness of some mechanical cores has been impaired by their "rigidity" (*i.e.,* they have dictated an arrangement of fixtures which is adaptable to a limited variety of room setups). An example might be Fuller's "prefabricated bathroom" of 1938, designed to be pressed as a single unit—fixtures, walls, and floors—out of sheet aluminum. And some would seem to have been almost too thorough in conception, like the excellent Ingersoll Utility Unit sold by Borg-Warner in the middle forties, which included all the utilities mentioned before, together with all bathroom fixtures, refrigerator, stove—and the kitchen sink.

Still and all, there is no question that the development and variation of prefabricated

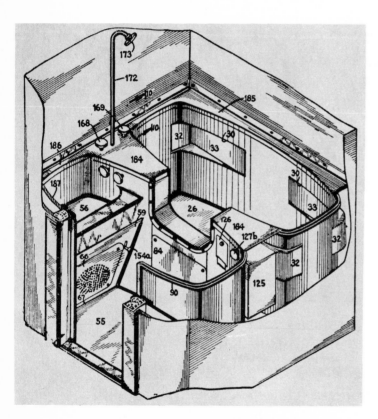

Patent Drawing for the Integrated Fuller Bathroom

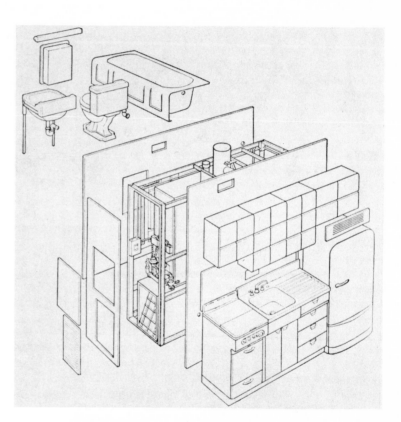

Exploded Drawing of the Ingersoll Utility Unit

mechanical-core arrangements is one of the most promising fields for experiment. The question is more exactly how far to go with them. And in our present study we have come across one application of mass-production steel technique which is entirely conjectural as yet—it must not be taken as a practical, proven, development—but which, to me at least, is a fetching idea. It would consist simply of taking two large sheets of metal, and stamping them—and then joining them together by welding or adhesives to form a plumbing wall containing in itself the drainage and supply lines for a complete bathroom. The method is somewhat

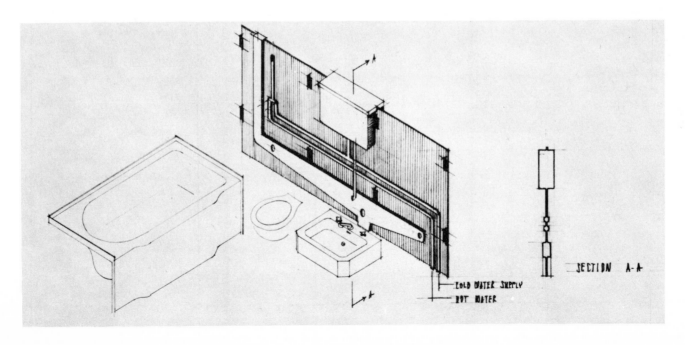

COLD WATER SUPPLY
HOT WATER

SECTION A-A

analogous to the way in which refrigerator tubing is now formed, or to the use of printed circuits in electronic equipment. Each sheet would be formed in one stamping, and the stamping itself would reinforce the structure as a whole. If developments of this sort can be made practical, and if bathroom fixtures themselves can be "rationalized" into better machine shapes, it is likely that the bathroom which now costs $750 to hitch together could be retailed at about one third of that amount.

In searching after new uses for steel—the above are only a few examples—the architect must be guided by a different set of rules than he would use for many other materials. When, for instance, he tries to discover the *cost* of something—a steel floor, or roof or fencing system, a steel sandwich panel, or a rolled-on coating for a steel surface—he may be confused as well as delighted to find that costs vary widely according to the peculiar economy of machine use. He can discard almost *no* solution out of hand on the simple basis that it feels expensive to him. And in designing, say, a wall panel, he is obliged to think somewhat "big" about just what, by golly, an ideal wall should be: insulative, indestructible, decorative, easy of maintenance, and so on. Because, with volume methods, there may just be a way of making it so—and cheaply.

I can think of two examples. One comes from several years back, from our many-sided experience with Lustron. There was a point during that venture when we were asked by Carl Strandlund, president of the company, to design a motor-operated, self-raising-and-lowering sort of window for each room of the Lustron house. It was Mr. Strandlund's idea that such a window had pleasant advertising and sales possibilities. We agreed to that much, but pointed out at some length, patiently, that an automatic window was of no great utility, outrageously expensive—a luxury item, in short—and it had no place in a house designed for the many.

Mr. Strandlund listened obligingly for a while, and then sent us on our way with the instruction that he *liked* the idea of an automatic window, and he would just as soon have us stop arguing and *design* one. We did so unwillingly. And found out that while the electric motor and all the special gadgets necessary to make a window power-driven were indeed expensive in lots of two, ten or a hundred, produced in the quantities which Lustron would use, they came out to cost $3.50 per assembly. That is, very little more than the cost of ordinary hardware on the conventional hand-operated, push-'em-up type of window. And that is the sort of thing, clearly, which a big industry, and *only* a big industry, can do: codify complex hand operations into machine processes; invest ten thousand or ten million dollars in the mechanical preliminaries to production; and then, in spite of this monstrous beginning expense, turn out plastic piping or copper wire or steel track, at a rate of speed which brings them back close to "basic" materials cost.

The second example, somewhat analogous to that of the bathroom, comes from our present activity for National. In hunting about for the kind of wall surface for which every housewife lusts, we have come across a particular combination of sheet plastic with light-gauge sheet steel which would appear to hold infinite promise. The trouble is that, as it is now fabricated, it costs $0.60 per square foot, and that would seem to rule it out. Yet this trouble tends to retreat if, looking into things, we discover that the sheet steel involved costs only $0.075 a square foot, the plastic costs $0.02, and the adhesive which joins them costs $0.03; and that the difference between that total-materials cost of $0.125 and the $0.60 price is accounted for by the inefficiency of the press process by which the material is assembled, and by the fact that current demand is so very low.

So that, if such a material continues to appear practicable as a panel surface, the matter of exploiting its potential may be reducible to several problems, all of which have to be nudged along at the same time: to develop the panels into an architectural-design system which makes sense; to promote and market the material in such fashion as to create an adequate public demand; and to refine the machine system which turns it out so that, at hazard, a half-mile roll of plastic might be joined to a half-mile roll of sheet steel in a total elapsed time of half a minute. *Then* its price might well be something like 25 per cent of what it is at present, and its virtues as a material might bring it into competition at advantage with current wall products. But it takes a bit of doing.

There is another characteristic or paradox of mass-production methods, as they apply to residential housing, which I think will begin to exert a fundamental influence. It is that

EXHIBITION HOUSE   LIVING ROOM FROM ADULT COURT

Entrance court of
National Steel Exhibition House

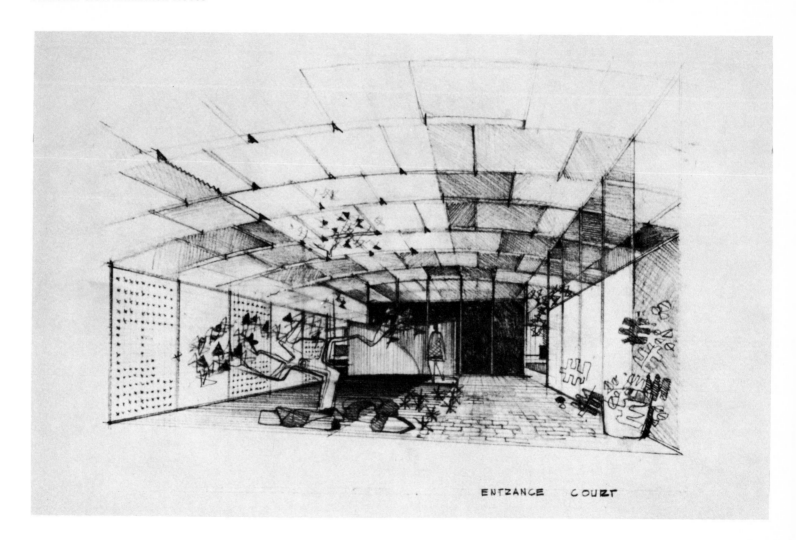

ENTRANCE COURT

at the same time one aspires to reduce the number and complexity of components, in order to keep down the investment in special machinery, one must seek to increase possible uses and combinations of components, so that the machines may operate at high volume—which often leads back toward complexity. Wrongly resolved, these two contrary tendencies lead to forced solutions like the Lustron bathtub machine. Rightly understood, I think they must lead to the kind of modernization and components marketing of which I spoke in the second chapter—the business of the young couple with the parts-of-house catalog, making an individual choice among, and assembly of, house components which are themselves fairly complex, large-sized, *and* standardized.

There is one other lesson which has been mentioned before, but which our present assignment has served to emphasize and which may be worth a final underlining. It is clear that steel can serve many purposes in small-house building which it has not served before. But the same holds true for many other materials. And our instructions have not been simply to find out everything a house does and how to do it just with steel. It becomes increasingly sure, as architecture, machine methods, and prefabrication advance together, that this progress at bottom does not consist in the duplication of each other's products by competing industries, but in the discovery of the best combinations of different basic products. It is a matter of communication almost as much as it is one of competition. Building, which is complicated enough to start with, is becoming so immensely more so that

**Architectural rendering of
Hartford, Conn., steel redevelopment housing
by Carl Koch Associates**

the problems of "spreading the word" do not exist merely between producer and consumer. They exist between producer and builder, producer and developer, supplier, architect—and producer and producer as well. Product development—research—consists, often enough, just in finding the man to give the answers to questions he didn't know anyone had to ask. It is a business of *excitation*—one company persuading the next to undertake *now* the project they had always rather meant to get to. The steel people stimulating the asphalt people to discover a new wet-applied method for coating a steel-shingle system; the plastic people to perfect an adequate rolled-on finish for wall panels; the plywood people to develop proper adhesives for joining wood and metal in floor systems. A steel exhibition house, if we eventually design one, should properly include many new and exciting uses for other products, just as the exhibition houses of other industries, in some cases unwittingly, have had recourse to the special capacities of steel. I am reminded of an exploration we made recently through one of the aluminum houses. Our guide, at one point, halted beside a support post—a lovely affair—and thwacked it proudly with his palm. "This," he said, "is of anodized aluminum in a special combination with lifetime impregnated wood." "Yes," we asked, "but what holds it up?" "Oh, well," he said, blinking at it cautiously, "of course it has a steel column inside."

11 Mighty Thoughts

This is the last chapter. Time for conclusions, and for odds and ends of things I meant to include earlier.

I have been traveling recently. First to an "automotive center"—a sort of combination park, museum, pleasure dome, and memorial, established in its own honor by one of the big automobile companies. And then, by chance, to a speculative real-estate development—a small community for old people, in Florida. And my feelings, as I toured these places, were somewhat the reverse of what is architecturally right and proper.

The automotive center was Real Architecture. Here were many of the nice things I have spoken about: wide reaches of ground and promenade, fountains and statuary, expanses of window, and pretty girls in cool uniforms. Here were artistry, finish, sculpture of spaces—an admirable display of things we teach in architectural schools—together with the technical enlightenment and heavy money necessary to "put it across," as they say on Madison Avenue. And so well constructed is the whole affair that, centuries hence, it may be all that remains of us. Archaeologists will scrape off the ashes and search out the ground plans, and architects will set out to recapture its glories in their own work. "Neo-contemporary," the style will be called.

Twinges of doubt. This is (and for a long time will be) one of the fine buildings of

America, but I felt a curious paradox between the building and its uses; in this wealth of design sheltering a poverty of good sense.

I felt a different set of misgivings the next day, on a trip through one of the automobile plants and the city around it. It was not simply that the car in question was relatively cramped inside, wide, long, and overpowered—resembling, in fact, an unnatural relationship between two cars—or that the people who produced it were obviously uninterested in their work, and might well be. It was more something which had diffused out from the factory through the neighborhoods in which the workers had housed themselves—the neat brick ranchburgers with the tiny, excruciatingly green lawns. A sense of enclosure, passivity; the acceptance of tolerably comfortable circumstance; the use of energy toward conformity; the making of choices but not, in a way, decisions.

Then the real-estate development in Florida. This, like the factory, was established on the profit motive. A builder had bought 220 acres of land, was putting up small houses on speculation, and offering them for sale to old people who had a little money saved and a fairly sure idea of what they wanted. There was nothing special about the land—a retired grapefruit orchard about five miles inland along an estuary, out of the high-priced sections. The site planning and the houses themselves were "pretty good," an architect would say; a little cluttered. Nothing outstanding, nothing here to compare with the automotive shrine. But there was a boat landing and a community hall, and a person could grow a garden if he wanted. In spite of the fact that the residents were old and presumably meditative, there was a greater sense of interest and occupation here and far less contemplation of surfaces than in the other places—more than could be explained away by the fact that here we had the uses of leisure, and there the stern business of making things go. Here, it seemed to me, builder and architect had reason to be proud.

My feelings here may not appear to conform with much of what I have said in preceding chapters. I have argued, after all, that the procedures of building must be better geared to this age, and that design must be better geared to those procedures. Surely the automotive center would seem to stand for *that*. I have said that the business of making homes is best approached on a machine basis. The factory might seem to symbolize *that*. And the neighborhoods around it might be taken to be what you get if you gather people together to serve a factory's purposes.

But I think there are distinctions to be made, and implications in them for the architect, executive, builder, and buyer. While, out of my own experience, they come incomplete, vague, and perhaps familiar, I can only offer them as a "sense" of things.

The difference between the old peoples' settlement and, say, the automotive center seems to me describable, first of all, as one of humanity. The center is perfect, so to speak; the answer of the experts. There is nothing about it that an individual might feel called on to change around or add to. Whether, as its planners likely believe, it asserts the character of the machine age, or whether it asserts the planners, it is at any rate assertive. The settlement, on the other hand, is eternally *un*finished, being improved on by the settlers—or anyway, pushed around—rough surfaced and, in places, unapologetically messy. It has samenesses in it. The houses look somewhat alike, or did at the start. But it is an unobtrusive sameness which makes available other, more important things, and gives itself to change. Architect and builder have provided a start to participation, involvement, and improvisation, and then stepped aside.

Surely, if we have contributed anything to history, it is a heightened regard for the individual; a confidence in man as equal to his situations; a belief in people, not things; and in *doing,* as much as the thing done. And if, in our use of machines, we find ourselves in circumstances we had not reckoned on, we do not find our way out by building mystiques about the machine, as has been done in the automotive center. Neither do we preserve our individualities by hopeful, expensive imitations of handicraft—as in the workers' houses—nor by a fearful, belligerent assertion that nothing important has happened to us.

Because, obviously, it has. Mass production affects not simply the manufacture and distribution of some of our products. It is not only an organization of mechanical forces, but of people. It influences not only our work patterns—the carrying on of mail-order work, or research, or journalism—but our close emotional ties. (Children, by example, are no longer economic assets, and most of the economic forces which made the family relationship an automatic and natural one can no longer be relied on.) At one and the same time it has made it possible for us to live widely, comfortably, and constructively, and has crimped us into our wee houses, side by each; increased the hazards of our trying, individually, to do better for ourselves, and even obscured our realization that there is a better to do. (I have met people who *enjoyed* living on eye level with the freeway—they made a game of counting license plates. And I am reminded of a remark made to me by some clients of a fine modern architect, which I'm sure would disturb him: "He's such a wonderful man. We don't dare change anything from where he put it." These two families lived in very different surroundings, but they shared the same passivities.)

How to scrutinize our circumstances, how to select the useful elements—what constrictions to accept for the sake of breaking through others? How, specifically, to help people get into good houses?

I am willing to believe, for reasons touched on before, that the traditional entrepreneur pattern of land development will not give us answers enough. And I take it that since the matters of a single house and lot and household are increasingly intermixed with those of the community around it, the individual buyer is more and more outnumbered when it comes to determining the character of the place he wants to live in. For both these reasons, what we fondly call "large solutions" are in order. At the same time, I discover few virtues in solutions so large that they must be imposed and financed by government, dictated by the experts, and rolled out at further cost to private initiative.

A solution need only be large enough to "spread the risk" adequately, to consolidate some of the piecemeal aspects of construction work, and to provide sizable, recoverable sums of money at those points where sizable money is needed—mainly at the outset of things. We are prone to say that the risks of land development are great; they are great only in sequence, and in comparison to the capacity of the individual developer. There is a constant, general pressure for housing, and ability to pay for it, and these can be made to provide an effective, generalized response to the fluctuations and ground tremors of a particular undertaking. There are many such middle-ground solutions, and no reason to neglect any of them. My own set of prejudices runs in favor of the formation of buyers' groups.

There is infinite variety to the size of buyers' groups, the ways in which they may be —and have been—established, the extent of the land development and construction involved, and the extent to which they act in concert. At one end of the scale, we could say, are the two families who band together to buy a certain piece of land—perhaps securing favorable terms from a lawyer to cover the matter of title search—and then divide it up according to prior agreement and proceed individually. At the other end, hypothetically, would be an extreme cooperative arrangement in which the buyers act as a group from first to last; develop the land from the beginning, perhaps doing some of the work themselves; put up identical houses; and control a number of community facilities in concert, even to the extent of shops and other commercial activities. (In between there are a great number of schemes, varying from real cooperatives to what are called speculative-builder co-ops, which are cooperative in name only and formed with the purpose of obtaining advantageous government-insured financing.)

The savings in the first example given will presumably be small, and in the second, hopefully, large. The advantages in cost, and the liabilities, and the points at which advantage in bargaining power may be sufficient to justify the surrender of individual discretion (as well as those occasions where it probably *isn't*), are matters which should be clearly stated at the outset and clearly scanned by those who consider joining up; they are matters which differ in particular but not in nature from all joint enterprises in all times—the voyages of the Puritans or a woolly-bear hunt.

As a matter of social order, it would seem to be desirable for the function of all buyer groups that at the end of the mortgage period, if not before, the individual buyer should be in clear possession of house and land; the right to bargain by himself for its resale; or, as suggested by the Belmont town official, to paint it in green and red stripes if he damn well likes, and let his lawn grow to crab grass.

As a matter of common sense, and of practical and legal advantage, most associations of buyers settle between the two extremes before mentioned. All need some starting point around which to form: land (as in the case of Snake Hill); or a produced house (as in the case of buyers' groups who have made use of Techbuilt); or a combination of land, proposed site plan, and house design, as with Conantum. There will always be some elements of the housing process with respect to which it is best to rely on hired experts—where group participation is likely to result only in confusion. Fine, small legal points are one example, or excavation work, or intricacies of house design, and, indeed, all but the general aspects of site planning. But the buyer group may legitimately insist, and should, on full information along the way, a maximum choice of alternatives, and the reservation to itself of critical decisions. It is in a good position to bargain in advance for a high level of performance—most architects and builders will jump at the chance. There will always be uncertainties; Conantum has given examples. Yet, as in the case of Conantum, the savings to buyers and the final achievement may be notable. And there need not again be as many uncertainties as Conantum embraced. The clear lessons of that enterprise can be interpreted in favor of a hard, contractual basis of procedure (particularly in the building process), clear definition of responsibilities, and an absolute minimum of brotherly love.

Cooperatives have been mentioned before as one variety of buyer association. They have been growing in usefulness and the regulations governing them have become less complex. It is true that the history of building cooperatives to date has been an uneven one: On the one hand they have sometimes come under attack as examples of creeping socialism; on the other hand many of the "cooperatives" built so far have not been true cooperatives at all—their developers have extricated the usual hearty profit before turning them over to the eventual owners. Nevertheless, there are so many clear advantages to cooperative development and ownership, ranging over everything from the cost of garaging—or of plumbing—to the length of amortization period, that cooperative techniques are bound, soon, to prove out. The cooperative seems the best method to date to combine the psychological advantages of home ownership—the feeling that one is working for *one's self* and not the landlord—with the economies of large-scale rental enterprises. The perils of cooperative ventures, though real, are not much different in kind from those which mark *all* building activity. Concerning them, to be sure, there is a very considerable need for public information and private technical assistance: the first reaction of the individual citizen to the suggestion that he himself might initiate or engage in a cooperative is likely to be a simple "Who—me?" But it seems reasonable to hope that private foundations will recognize precisely this—the giving of information and the provision of recoverable funds—as a good use of their resources. And, ways have already been discovered, as witness the work of the United Housing Foundation in the New York metropolitan area.

In relation to buyer groups, whether cooperatives or not, it seems to me that private corporations too have opportunity to take a somewhat more active role than in the past. Many corporations have. Others are fearful of appearing to "take over" from already established communities, or feel they already have enough worries of their own, without getting into the housing dodge. But it is the movement of industry which determined the general course of land development; to leave the settlement of industrial personnel to work itself out may be, in some cases, to scant responsibility. Or it may invite problems of absenteeism and low efficiency which—as in the case of Willow Run in World War II—it is worth much to avoid. The respects in which corporations or foundations can engage in the housing process are, again, various. One way which appears to have real promise for the future involves a new sort of entrepreneur who calls himself a large-scale developer. He very likely started as a real-estate broker, and turns into this new community-building catalyzer by the following steps: He finds land for the large company looking for a new factory; he arranges to get the factory built for the new company; he may even agree to rent the factory to the big company, relieving it of all the headaches of ownership and providing it with a number of mysterious tax advantages; he may further agree to help the factory owner provide good housing for his executives and employees. To do this he starts hiring or, at least, encouraging builders. Frequently he finds himself having to provide water supply, sewage disposal, new highways, a whole community plan. He finds himself juggling a group of home owners who need a big shopping center to encourage them to come to this new community with a group of shop owners who need a positive market before they move there. This kind of operation raises the question, Who is doing what to whom?—but in the few cases where this is resulting in new towns planned from scratch, the benefits over the "grow-like-Topsy" method are obvious. In the example given, the main point is this: that the money used is recoverable although certainly, for a period, risk money. In our growth economy, it is unlikely to work any long-term damage to established interests.

To come back to the architect and designer. What are his responsibilities in the emerging building pattern—and, in the most general sense, to this age?

In the first place, to say it outright, the architect really doesn't know very much about machines, and he needs to learn. He can get by, of course. (Two tokens of his getting by are that he seldom bothers any more to design a house costing less than thirty thousand dollars —and that a house should cost thirty thousand dollars.) For years he has paid lip service to the Bauhaus statement of 1923, "We want an architecture adapted to our world of machines, radio, and fast motor cars—buildings which are to be thought of as outgrowths of modern technique and design, may be considered as an assembly of prefabricated and standardized parts, so applied as to fulfill the varying requirements of those to be housed." But the buildings he designs are handsome repetitions of those designed, as a beginning, *then*. He will adapt himself this far to the machine: he will ask whether the machine will do a piece of work he wants it to. And, yes, the answer usually is, it can. But that is not always to say that this is what the machine can do most easily, cheaply, and well.

This architectural habit of mind is often supported by the machine men themselves, as at Lustron, for example, where our first instructions were to design the house, and let *them* worry about how to make it. One of the significant problems of today's industry—not simply in housing—is the gap between design and production.

We have a picture in our mind's eye of what machine work "looks like," or is supposed to: even, shiny, smooth, geometric, etc. The designers themselves have helped to foster this picture. The automotive center is a sophisticated portrayal of it—a representation of a representation. But the picture is only half accurate. Machine work can as well be uneven, rough-surfaced, and irregular. It is typical, for instance, that one machine may turn out a piece which, "roughed in"—imperfect to the machinist's eye—is still entirely adequate for the use to which it will be put. It is functionally perfect. But then, in order to make it match our picture of what machine work must be, to put the "finishing touches" on the piece, three other machines turn out to be necessary—adding as much again in complexity and cost. This is a kind of machine aesthetics, an *expertise,* which the designer is guilty of encouraging simply because he seldom exerts himself to find out about it and suggest differently.

To give another example, again from Lustron: The process of enameling the Lustron steel panels in color was an immensely skillful one. So was the process of quality control involved—of making sure that each panel was evenly, smoothly enameled, and a perfect match to the fifty or five hundred panels preceding. It was immensely expensive, too, and it sometimes happened that a whole batch of panels came out wrong—that is to say, somewhat uneven of color, or a shade too light or dark—and had to be tossed away. Considering all this, we made a suggestion to the producer in charge: that since the "wrong" panels could do everything a panel was supposed to, and since their unevenness of color itself was interesting and decorative, why not use the wrong panels along with the "right" ones, and give some variety to a wall surface which, all perfect, was likely to be a touch unexciting. In fact, since he found the control of quality to be an exacting task, why not do it a lot more easily and cheaply, and let the "wrong" panels happen on purpose. The suggestion seemed natural enough to us, but the producer all but threw us out of the shop. We had asked him to cast away his professional reputation, and twenty years of painful experience. In a way, of course, his attitude was admirable, but it must be related to the question of what is craftsmanship and what, in the last analysis, is not.

To the designer, oriented as he is toward the Piazza di San Marco, the business of learning about roll shapes and electrostatic spraying may appear a trifle dull. It is. Sometimes it's *awfully* dull. Take the designer who wants to plan a simple window for mass production. He will not only be concerned with its proportions, the good look of its hardware, or the fact that it shouldn't leak. He will have to deal with the material of which the frame is made—steel, wood, aluminum—and more than that, with the ways in which the material is best worked. If it is steel, he must know the different implications for design in cold rolling or hot rolling, drop forging, or bending or brake-forming. He must consider the number of units in the frame to be separately formed, the design of them for forming, and the machinery and techniques necessary to join them, once formed. The window is to be pre-finished and pre-glazed—he must consider the order of machinery necessary for this. At the same time he will have to provide for *other* sizes of window—how many of the parts he has designed will still be useful in other dimensions? And then there are matters of warehousing and shipping: The window must be light, easy to handle, it should nest, it should pack well, it should resist damage to its edges in transit. And finally, application: If the window is to be saleable in a large market, it has to look and fit equally well into a wall of brick, or wood, or steel, or aluminum, or stone, or whatever. Back he goes to the drawing board.

Slow work—very. But it is the kind of work toward which the designer's responsibilities are carrying him. If he doesn't concern himself with this manner of problem, someone else will have to, someone without his particular regard for proportion. And the result, for the small window, will be the same as it now is for the small house. The designer, for fear of boredom or difficulty, will have let ugliness win again by default.

The architect must be willing to function as technician, machinist, builder, and boilermaker. It is the only way in which, as artist, he may hope to maintain control of his work, and to leave his impress upon it. It behooves him to think what that impress should be; by so doing, I think, he will discover other obligations—some I have already, partly, suggested.

The thing which an architect designs—if he functions effectively in a large market—will be built several or thousands of times over. It had best be versatile and capable of variation. This is partly because the thing, whatever it is, will be delivered into a variety of circumstances. And it is partly, as already mentioned, because of the desire, and need, for individuality. But on this second count, the architect will have to decide what kinds of individuality he may best serve, and *whose* individuality, and separate the appearance of individuality from the practice of it.

Individuality is not well manifested by the conventional small house of today, nor by many of the unconventional large ones. (It is curious that in both instances the individuality achieved by the owner is someone else's.) Yet the urge to show individuality is legitimate. And even in a mass-production world the architect may hope to give it scope. Modularization of components has already been discussed as one, most evident, way. But I can imagine that we will discover other architectural shapes, and materials not modularized but still capable of rearrangement. Baggy shapes, for instance; as the boxlike metal-and-glass vision of the future embodied in the automotive center proliferates, we shall be in desperate need of relief.

But there are aspects of individualism infinitely more important than the manifestation, or appearance, of it. And the architect will not serve these with all his interchangeable, mechanical cunning, and artistry, if he arrogates to himself the arrangement of things, settles on complete architectural answers, and parcels them out. He must so devise his work that the buyer is invited into the planning process. He cannot do so by laboring to maintain the traditional architect-client relationship. That relationship is already beyond the means of most home buyers, and will become increasingly more so. (And even in the best of circumstances it often consists of the architect listening patiently to his clients' wants—long enough to make them feel good—and then, with glazed eye, wandering back to the drafting room and doing what he would have done anyway.) The ways in which the architect *can* hope to engage the interest and participation of the buyer are many. All of them, to my mind, involve a simple resolution to design not architectural answers but architectural *means;* to accept more fully the architectural significance of the things which happen in and to a house after it is first drawn and first built; and to forswear the presumption of trying to prescribe them. He must undertake, obviously, to deliver an adequate package of things: a full complement of walls, roof, and windows, a generous and graceful share of space, and in this, perhaps, a suggestion of the activities he believes are pleasing to man—a design which, if never added to, is still sufficient. But what he designs should be capable of addition and rearrangement and change, long after he has palmed his check and passed on to a more permanent reward.

A resolution of this kind has its immediate, tangible applications. And it welcomes an active, restless, creative, and ambitious attitude on the part of the client—or buyer, or owner, or if we want to call him so, the public. For the architect it may have less tangible, equally important results. He may find that he moves—and gladly—toward a quietness or even anonymity of design, a conception of design itself as educative rather than didactic, the provision of fair beginnings. That architecture may express, portray, dramatize or commemorate the business of our living together—is only incidental. First of all it should make it possible.